# IT'S ALL GOOD

# Colossal Conversations
## with
# SONNY
# ROLLINS

### Christine M. Theard, M.D.

Cover design: Tina Kirby

Cover painting: Yvonne Theard

Painting based on original photo by Chuck Stewart

ISBN 978-1-7325827-0-5 Hard copy
ISBN 978-1-7325827-1-2 Paperback
ISBN 978-1-7325827-2-9 eBook

Library of Congress Cataloging-in-Publication Data is available upon request.

They Are Divine Books
34145 Pacific Coast Highway #640
Dana Point, California 92629-2808

www.theyaredivinebooks.com
theyaredivinebooks@gmail.com

Printed in the United States of America
First Printing, 2018

To my beautiful and talented mother, Yvonne Theard, the artist who painted the cover of this book and the one who has painted love and grace all over our family for all of my life.

To my brilliant father Les Theard, who taught me at a young age that there were no limits to my dreams and that I could do anything that I wanted to do.

# Contents

# Authors Note

After I encouraged Sonny to share his personal thoughts and experiences with his fans, he asked me to write this book. His request revealed a calling for me to bring Sonny's inspiring words to his fans and to others.

Our regular phone conversations started with my intention to provide him assistance and advice as a medical doctor and family friend. In this time, Sonny became a potent positive force in my life. The wisdom he shared has been a precious gift that I am compelled to share with others.

Our conversations were a catalyst to my emotional, professional and spiritual development. After more than twenty years of busy cardiology practice, I expanded my education in the area of ancient spiritual concepts and natural healing methods.

I have taken this opportunity to share exciting data from western medical studies that have scientifically proven the benefits of ancient eastern healing practices. In the process of my continuing education, these topics came up frequently in our conversations. I have also shared my personal experiences that help to illustrate many of the concepts that Sonny discusses.

This invitation into our personal exchanges is an opportunity to get to know Sonny, elevate your spiritual understanding with him and enjoy him as I have.

Chapter 1

# The Beginning

When I walked into the performance hall, the vibration of excitement was immediately tangible. I was elated to finally see the great Sonny Rollins perform, but I sensed something more. I felt an energy in that hall that was exhilarating beyond my own anticipation. I guided my mom to our seats toward the front left. After getting settled into our long-reserved spots, I glanced at the people all around us.

This was an interesting crowd. I looked across a very eclectic group of jazz lovers with a broad representation of styles, types and ages - all of them rushing to get to their precious reserved spots. They seemed alive with the same sense of fervent excitement that I felt when I walked into the room. There were full smiles, bright eyes, chins up and erect postures, all of them energetically looking around the concert hall, adding to a collective anticipation.

I quickly realized what I was sensing. It was love. There was flowing, tangible love in the room. These were Sonny's devoted fans, and their adoring energy made me think about my dad, Les Theard. I missed him, and I wished that he had been there with us. A more appreciative fan than my father could not possibly exist in that room or anywhere else in the world. My father has a relationship with Sonny Rollins that spans four decades. I knew that he was going to miss something very special, and that my experience would have been so much better if he had been there with us.

Growing up in New Orleans, music was an integral part of Dad's life. He discovered at a young age that he was excited by the quality of live amateur music that was performed regularly in the streets around his home in the projects. Of course, many jazz greats performed in the city of New Orleans and he was thrilled, while a student at Xavier University, to serve as an usher for many of those concerts through a music program there. But it wasn't until 1962, five years after leaving New Orleans, that my father got to see Sonny perform live.

Dad graduated from Notre Dame with a PhD in Physical Chemistry and then stayed in South Bend, Indiana to do a postdoctoral year. His father was a huge proponent of education and was also an avid fan of Notre Dame football.

A very special event was planned for him to travel from New Orleans to attend a Notre Dame football game. With plans to be there early when my grandfather arrived by train, dad drove from South Bend to Chicago the night before. With some time that evening, he went out seeking live music. That's when he first found Sonny.

Sonny was playing at McKie's DJ Lounge. Dad recalls that he sat at the bar which was very close to the stage and vividly remembers that he was "bedazzled" by Sonny's performance. For many years he wished that he had taken advantage of that possible opportunity to meet Sonny. As a result, Dad developed a new resolve that allowed him to meet many great artists over the years, and he became known in our family to fear no barriers when it came to meeting musicians.

Meeting Sonny, though, did not happen until 14 years later when Dad was traveling for work in Bethesda, Maryland in 1976. That night he found Sonny performing in a small, intimate club. This time he decided to try to meet Sonny on the set break. He easily walked beyond the stage partition. And without struggle, he found Sonny -- quietly leaning against the wall with his sax.

Dad walked up and introduced himself, and he fondly recalls the open, easy nature of their conversation. This was the beginning of a long friendship. Over the years, Dad had numerous opportunities and travelled on many occasions to see Sonny's live performances.

I was a child during those times and, until the concert with my mother, I had not seen Sonny perform live. My personal awareness of "the Colossus" only consisted of a familiarity with multiple album covers that sat in our living room. There was the frequent sound of Sonny's music and other jazz music in our home throughout my childhood. But, at that time, I was not aware of which particular musician was associated with the songs that were played.

However, I knew Sonny's powerful, piercing gaze because I saw his eyes evolve on a canvas as my mother worked on his portrait. She is an artist and when we were kids she did portraits of a series of jazz musicians that included many of my father's favorites. I watched each of these works gradually take form on her canvas. As a child, I found some of these large facial images to be intimidating as Mom captured some intense and fierce looks, and she did so in a scale far larger than life. But with Sonny's portrait, I was drawn in. As his eyes took form, they looked very real and easily caught my attention as soon as I entered the room. The portrait seemed huge and Sonny's eyes were so large and strong. But along with the intensity, there was an open softness that Mom captured that was stirring and mysterious. Sonny looked intense, but also calm and endearing.

The portrait became a gift for Sonny. He was the guest of honor at a party that was arranged to celebrate him before his planned performance in Houston. My father wanted to share Mom's collection of jazz portraits with him. My Aunt Merle hosted a dinner party in her home with Creole cuisine that she prepared with my mother. The portraits were displayed. To our delight, Sonny chose to visit with our family rather than attend a large party planned by concert organizers.

Sonny meticulously viewed the paintings and gave extra pause to the portrait of his idol, Charlie Parker. He visited with the guests and mentioned to his nephew Clifton Anderson, the trombonist in his band, that my mother resembled a relative of theirs from the islands where his mother was born.

Then Sonny gave my mother a very special compliment. He told her that she had captured something in her portrait that he had not seen in the photograph that she had used as a guide. As an artist, this may have been the greatest compliment that he could have given to her. Later, as Sonny prepared to leave the party, she lifted his portrait from the mantle and presented it to him. Sonny appeared to be deeply touched.

Unfortunately, I missed it all. At that time, I was a four-hour drive away and deep in my work as the new physician in a large cardiology group practice. I was not able to leave town. My love for jazz was strong but I had no idea of what I was missing when I missed Sonny's performance and the special time that he spent with my family before his show.

While I was not actively involved, I was aware of the value of the friendship that Sonny had with both of my parents. Dad saw him regularly in Europe at various jazz festivals, but Mom did not see him for a long time. After relocating across the country to California (and nearly 20 years later), I learned that Sonny was performing close to our home.

I was determined to reunite what I saw as old friends. I wanted to set up a plan for the visit prior to the night of the show. In spite of all the history of my family's interactions with Sonny, I felt very lucky when I received a message from Sonny's website advising me to take Mom backstage and ask for Sonny's road manager. I planned to do exactly as I had been directed. As I sat there feeling the excitement around me, looking forward to my first live Sonny Rollins experience, I thought about how fortunate I was to also be able to look forward to meeting the Colossus after the show.

When Sonny emerged on stage he had the persona of a rock star. He was wearing a bright red shirt that contrasted with his big white hair and beard. His fans welcomed him like a rock star with a standing ovation before he played a single note. He was charismatic and confident, and he humbly accepted the ovation. Then, he started playing. The crowd was ecstatic.

Very quickly, I understood the anticipation that had been

in the room. I was immediately taken into the fury. This was a cosmic flight for all willing and wanting to join in, with Sonny as the conductor and his sax as the vehicle. The direction was up and out. It wasn't Sonny just playing a horn. It was Sonny taking us on a musical journey with his horn. He played this instrument as if it was an integral part of his being. It danced up, down and around with flowing ease, like it was feather light and seamlessly attached to him. I had seen many seasoned pros play the sax before, but not like this. Not even close to this.

I recognized many of the songs that were played. But Sonny's improvisation, of course, was real time. It was a creative gift especially for this audience. It was happening right there, right then. As a life-long jazz fan, I had been to many live performances. This was my first Sonny experience and it was extraordinary. I knew I was very fortunate to be a witness to it. The love and adoration from the fans around me just solidified my appreciation.

I became aware of the reason for the love and adoration from the fans around me. I also became aware that I had missed opportunities to see Sonny for many years and this time felt very precious. I decided to not let that happen again. The buzz that I felt when we walked in had evolved and grown into a loud roar during the show.

After the performance, as the crowd cleared the room, there remained a quieter hum with reverence and awe-filled space. Feeling like a new fan, I wanted more at the end of the show. I sat there wide eyed for a moment and then suddenly remembered my important mission to get Mom backstage.

I had to find the way through the fan obstacles to get there. There was no apparent access to the stage in the performance hall. We made our way to the foyer and I looked around the sides of the front area for doors that might provide entry to the back. There were none. I realized this was not going to be easy. People were exiting very quickly. I searched for anyone that looked like they could be associated with the show, and I saw people in jackets that identified them to be employees of the performance hall.

I spotted a petite middle-aged lady at the door and headed her way with Mom. She smiled pleasantly as we approached her, and as I introduced myself and my Mom. I explained that Mom was a friend of Sonny's and that I had promised to take her back stage to see him. I asked for her help. Her smile disappeared. She responded with a very serious look and detailed directions. She advised us to go out of the theater, to the right, down the stairs, around the side, around some trucks, back to the loading area where we would find the entry door to the backstage.

We headed out on our mission. The stairs were easy to find. We went down slowly accommodating Mom's back and knee problems. When we got to the bottom we could see many large trucks but no obvious path to backstage. My Mom looked at me with some concern. I didn't like what I saw either but responded positively, "Let's go Momma. I said I'd take you to see Sonny, and we will find him." We headed slowly around the trucks. When we got around the trucks there was a large loading area with several large garage size doors and no obvious entryway for guests or performers. It was everything but inviting. But at that moment, I felt a strange resolution. The resolution was that I am my father's daughter and I will get backstage.

We were dressed for the performance and I was wearing high heels. There with my mother, I suddenly started to laugh because I felt so ridiculous in my heels standing in a dark loading zone. Certainly, the area was not designed for visitors to walk through.

My laughing seemed to calm Mom and we both lightened up and laughed at how silly we felt. Taking a guess on the best option I said, "Let's go this way," and with our heels clanging on the metal stairs we headed up a flight that ended at some doors. I tried the first and second doors with no luck. I grabbed onto the third door handle and pulled. It opened... I sighed... and we walked in. We headed down a hall and quickly encountered a security guard who asked if we needed help. I mentioned the road manager and told him that we had been advised to ask for him. He turned and pointed as the manager was walking into that area at that exact moment.

I introduced myself to the manager and I was quickly relieved when he recognized my last name. He broke out a huge smile and told me that he had just seen my uncle, Lowell Theard the night before in LA. Lowell is my father's identical twin brother who lives and practices internal medicine in Los Angeles. Very warmly and without pause, the manager took us directly to an area where a small group of fans were waiting for Sonny to come out of his dressing room.

People were talking quietly and waiting patiently. We stood right at the end of a short hall that led to the dressing room door. Mom was standing ahead of me and could see the door.

After about twenty minutes Mom broke out a big smile and I heard Sonny say, "Yvonne is that you?" The soft chatter in the room stopped completely as Sonny and Mom had a breathtaking reunion. He spoke to her as if they were alone in the room.

The other people in the room continued to be silent and did not disturb this meeting. They were still and watched as Sonny talked to my mother. There was a sweet and lovely interaction between them which was in full view of the other fans. It was obvious that this was a friendship with much mutual affection.

I felt that for a moment I disappeared into the rest of the group as they were facing each other and speaking very softly. Like a fan, I was taking pictures while Sonny asked my Mom about the family and about my father. He asked her about her painting and about whether she was happy living in California.

I felt the glare of the observers getting stronger in the near silence of the room. Mom reached out her hand toward mine and introduced me to Sonny. He gave me a warm, strong hand shake and a family hug.

Again, like a real fan, I asked for a picture with him and he sweetly complied. I was feeling a bit awestruck and couldn't find much to say. But, I did tell him that the show was wonderful and that I felt lucky to get to see him. He asked me whether I had been at the party that my aunt had in Houston. I was embarrassed to explain how my work caused me to miss the party and miss that special opportunity.

By then, the silence in the room felt like a roar. We said goodbye and stepped back. The other fortunate people in the room were waiting patiently and had respected our space during our short conversation. They moved forward as we left.

I felt immensely privileged that day. On the same day that I first became aware of the magnitude of Sonny's aura and the magic of his live performance, I got to be a part of this lovely reunion with my mother and to personally meet this musical master. His energy was brilliant.

As we walked to our car and drove home, I felt that something very important had happened that night. I was a new, far more aware fan of Sonny Rollins and I somehow knew that it was the beginning of something very special.

I was sure that I would see him again.

Chapter 2

# Suffering

*"If you did everything that you could,*
*that was your part.*
*You did what you were called to do.*
*You are successful.*
*What happens from there is not up to you."*

No time was wasted, less than a year later in the summer of 2012, I was off to Europe to join my father for a mini Jazz tour. Since his retirement he has pursued a life's dream with great success. For more than a decade, he has lived half of the year in Paris and the other half in his childhood home in New Orleans, Louisiana. It has been his summer routine to travel around Europe attending numerous Jazz festivals. Over these years I had received multiple invitations to join the fun. But, my responsibilities made it seem impossible to take the time to go to Europe. After my new inspiration, this year I made it happen. I planned a trip to join my father at the Umbria Jazz Festival in Italy and Jazz d'Antibes in Juan les Pins in the south of France. Sonny was a headliner at both events.

The performance site at the Umbria Jazz Festival in Perugia Italy was a very large stadium that seated about 5,000 people. Sonny performed in this huge venue with the flair of a rock star. It was the largest jazz festival performance that I had ever seen.

While the event in Umbria was the largest, the one in Antibes was the most beautiful I had ever attended. The stage sits close to the edge of the beach and has the breathtaking French Riviera as it's backdrop. The atmosphere was mesmerizing. The sun was floating down on the horizon as Sonny did his soundcheck and it cast a magical light on the stage. We watched as its reflection danced on Sonny's horn as he rehearsed. Then we found the best seats in the place to watch the show. Right there on the wing of the stage. It felt like a dream as we watched the phenomenal show.

When it was done I joined Dad waiting to visit Sonny. There were quite a few people ahead of us. But after a short while we stepped inside a door and could see Sonny sitting quietly and comfortably greeting his guests. When it was our turn, my Dad walked in and sat directly next to him. He introduced me, and I sat directly across from Sonny who remembered that we had met. They talked a while about Dad's new project, a mentoring program to encourage and inspire kids in lower income areas to do well in school and aim for college. Sonny expressed his interest in participating in the program.

Before this night we had heard the band members express concern in regard to Sonny's health. Dad inquired about Sonny's health and told him that he was concerned. Then he reminded him that I was a physician.

Sonny turned his attention to me and noted that he had not remembered that fact. I assured him that I was capable and experienced and then I told him that I would be honored to check on him to provide an educated ear and medical advice if needed. I volunteered to be his advocate. He was pleased and said that he would love to hear from me.

Not long after that trip, I started calling Sonny regularly. All of our conversations were very interesting and special. While I started the calls with an intention to check on his health, I was routinely entertained, educated, touched and inspired by him. Our friendship developed quickly and continues to grow. I always look forward to our talks and I miss him when we have not spoken for some time.

Sonny always checked on me, asking about how I was

doing and whether I was taking care of myself. He shared his deep thoughts with me and similarly I felt I could share my thoughts and personal concerns with him. Over time, he became a regular support system for me.

Sonny's high intellect was clear. His crisp recollections and rapid responses were a pleasure. He was always very present in our conversations and I could hear his full attention and feel his positive intentions. It was a warm, authentic interaction that always flowed easily and naturally.

There were regular moments of humor in which I was consistently delighted by Sonny's laugh. When Sonny finds something amusing, he lets out a strong, bellowing "Ha, ha, ha, ha…!" His laugh is strong, full, and authentic. You feel it and it's impossible not to smile when you hear it.

In one of our early conversations, Sonny shared with me his deepest thoughts about his personal suffering. I felt very touched and honored that he shared his feelings with me. His candid expression about his experience invited me to join him in this space of honesty. It was an opening in which I was compelled to share my experience.

I suffered from an ongoing emptiness and regret about the results of a long-term challenge that greatly complicated my life over many years. I had spent an immense amount of time, effort and money to achieve a positive result, but it failed. The result was devastating. Out of necessity, I had mastered the skill of putting this issue aside and moving forward day by day. But, in the midst of a routinely happy, productive life, I had moments of being tortured by thoughts about it. For many years, this mental file would intermittently surface from my memory and wreak havoc on my happiness. After some time suffering with it, I would successfully close the file again. I would manage to stuff it away where it waited for another day to unexpectedly flail open and scorch my heart. This day was one of those days.

After I expressed my feelings to Sonny, I was spellbound by his response. I could not speak for many moments. I tearfully listened to his words. That day he gave me a precious gift that changed my perception forever.

"Hello Chris. How are you? I got the new supply of Curcumin that you sent me."

Great. I really believe it will be helpful. This one has a very potent extract of turmeric.

"I believe that it has helped me."

It's a good anti-inflammatory with no significant side effects. I have many patients who are taking anti-inflammatory medications that can be harmful in regard to their hearts and kidneys. This is very effective for all kinds of aches and pains and inflammation.

"I have a lot of that. Will it make me feel like I am twenty-five again?"

Maybe thirty.

"Ha, ha, ha…. I can tell a difference."

Speaking of pain, Sonny, I am having an unusual day today. I want to ask you about your personal experience about suffering?

"Well, I could say that I suffer every day in a way because that is just a part of being here on the planet; It's part of my karma. I have to suffer because, for instance, I am not blowing my horn. I was able to escape all of the hard things of life by playing my horn. That is not available to me now, so in a sense that is suffering. I enjoyed playing for hours every day. I practiced every day of my life. I was always trying to improve, to get better. When I couldn't play, I had to figure out what I was here for.

But you know, It's all good. But, now, I don't feel comfortable describing not playing as suffering because the benefits of the journey outweigh the momentary inconvenience of feeling bad or not understanding. You know we are supposed to suffer. This is life. Suffering is ignorance. We don't know why. We can't understand. Why is this happening to me? That would be described as suffering, but it is also ignorance. So, it's no big thing."

When you say ignorance are you saying we don't understand why things happen? Do you think it's all part of our personal journey?

"All things are part of our journey. Even things that don't appear to be what we want. When we identify with the body and the mind we suffer. We perceive that we want something, or we should have something. This is the ego talking. This is not the higher self."

Are you saying we suffer loss that is perceived mentally or physically, rather than seeing the bigger picture from a higher perspective?

"Right. Exactly. But we are higher beings having a physical experience."

How can we detach from the daily feelings of suffering?

"I understand suffering because of loss of things that we perceive are important. I see why people feel that way. I felt that way when I could not play my horn. It took me over a couple of years to sort of come to grips with this new reality. But now I have. I still long to do what I have done all of my life. I am still thinking music in my head, I still think about musical patterns, about musical fingering on my instrument. That is still going to be there. It may always be there.

But as far as feeling that it's something that happened to me, ... and woe is me and all of this kind of stuff, no. No, no! I feel that this is my karma. There is some reason why this is my condition. There is always a reason. I will understand the reason one day. It is not my place to understand it now. But it is all part of my plan. I am still here. I am here on earth, I believe to unravel my Karma, to fulfill my purpose. And I have to face it like a man."

That is very powerful. You said that you play in your head. You are playing in your mind and in your spirit. We have always said that your music came from somewhere else. You are composing in your creative spirit. We can't hear it, but you can. Your spirit can hear it and it can still make you soar.

"Yes. Sure. Sure. Because it is something of a positive nature. I will grant you that there is a spiritual component of my thinking about it in my head. I have always gone to that place when I played my music. That is where it came from. It's all good."

Do you think that being unable to play has assisted you in your spiritual growth?

"I am sure it has. Because I am here. I am still on the planet. I am seeing it as something positive when it could have been negative. I am growing, and I have a lot to grow and learn. It is part of my spiritual growth and I am going to keep the faith. I haven't given up on playing again. But my thinking has evolved. I don't feel the same way as I did before. When I played I was searching to get to the place that was beyond my mind and my body. I got there regularly. I would play and get to a place where I would not think. I would try not to think. In that place the music would flow through me.

I felt that this was out of this world. It was a higher place than what is here. I knew this and sought to get there every time that I played. At first when I could not play, I mourned the loss of this experience. But now I have evolved to the point that I am living in that place all the time. I feel it every day. It is a place of higher vibration. I can get there with compassion and giving. It is beyond this world. I am grateful that I have evolved to this point. It has all been a part of my journey."

I hope that I can evolve in my feelings about my suffering.

"What is happening with you?"

We've talked about my oldest son before. You know about what has happened to him.

"Yes, but you have always described things to me with hope and faith that he will be okay."

Deep in my being, I know that he will be home one day and that he will be fine. I hold onto this intention and belief and it has helped me regularly. But I have to actively put it out of my mind every day. It's a very unnatural thing to do when you are concerned about your child. Suffering is here. It's here with me now. I suffer for the loss and I suffer in fear for him. I suffer for the loss of this moment that he is not here with me, this moment that I cannot see his face. Countless moments that he has missed. The love and the life with his siblings, his grandmother and the whole family. I suffer with fear for his safety. I know that he is not emotionally safe. I fear that he is not physically safe.

"This is very difficult"

Then there is my guilt. This is what hits me and eviscerates my calm. I could not protect him. He is a child. He had been honest. He told them what his father had done to him. He told them he didn't want to go back there. He told everyone the truth. What does that do to his heart and to his mind? How will he find peace in this?

"I can only imagine how you feel as a mother. This is terrible."

I also feel guilt when I put it aside. I have to put it aside every day and be happy for his siblings. I must make a happy life for them.

"Of course you do. That is what mothers do for their children. I am sure that you have done a great job being happy for the triplets. But your love is still with him. He knows your love. It is a part of him. You are connected, and that will never change. You have to keep doing what you are supposed to do. Your life journey, your plan. Right now it is with the triplets. It is with your patients."

But Sonny, sometimes it just hits me, and I have such sadness. I miss him. I want to talk to him, to see him. We all want to see him. There is so much lost time. I did all that I could. Spent all I had. Tried to help. But we failed. I failed.

"Well, Chris, you have to stop! Stop! You must stop this now. You have to put it aside. This is not the big picture. You have to let go of that. You are not in control of his karma.

What is happening to him is part of his journey. There is no way for you to know what is in his plan. There is a plan for him that is a universal plan. It is not your plan. It is happening for a reason. He will come out of it with some knowledge. Some growth. Some awareness. If you did everything that you could. You got the best help. You spent all you had. That was your part. You did what you were called to do.

Do you hear me?"

Yes, …I hear you.

"If you did everything that you could. That was your part. You did what you were called to do. You are successful. What happens from there is not up to you. You found the best people to help him. You did everything that you could think to do for him. You did it all.

YOU ARE successful! You are successful. What happened from there is not up to you. You have to think about the big picture. You have to stop thinking about the result. That is not your part. You did your part, you did your best. You are successful.

This will be a success for him in his karma and his life but that is up to him, not you. We all have to work through our karma. You did your best. You are successful."

On this day, after hearing about Sonny's suffering, I opened up and I tearfully told him about my deepest pain with an open and vulnerable heart.

As he spoke I felt a sense of connection that was beyond my understanding. I felt a space in my being that was filled with potential. While these words echoed in my chest and reverberated in my mind, I heard them deep in my soul. The energy of this connection miraculously soothed the ache in my heart and stopped the angst in my mind. His comments pierced through years of pain. They were like stitches that somehow began to heal my gaping wound.

There was no doubt that I had done my absolute best. After this conversation, the torturous feelings of guilt and suffering released their hold on me. I continued to focus on sending love and positive thoughts to my precious son. I continued to hold strongly to my good intentions and to the relentless sense of knowing deep in the core of my being that told me that he would be okay

# Chapter 3

# Opportunity

*"I am not interested in puffing myself
up and thinking about myself.
That would short circuit myself
and interfere with my process.
I am just a human being trying to find
out the reason that we are here.
How to live well and how to do well."*

Every moment is an opportunity to shift to awareness. Our senses can be tools that bring us to realize the beauty of the moment. One can choose to view what is around them with a cognizance of the colors, textures, shapes and dimensions of all the things in the environment. Just stopping and placing focus on listening can bring to the forefront the sound of the breath, the breeze, the rain, birds, animals and voices. The most simple, ever-present sound is the sound of the breath and listening to it naturally calms the mind.

Wrapping one's arms tightly across the front of the chest creates a self-hug and brings into awareness the quiet sensations of the skin, the feel of the clothes, the feel of the heart beating, and a warm sensation. All of these observations that typically go unnoticed bring this moment into focus.

Moments are places of infinite possibilities and opportunities to be present. There is immense value in being in that place for it is truly the only real thing that we have. The past is long gone, and the future does not exist. An appreciation of the value of each moment improves the quality of life because it frees us from the past. These are only memories that suddenly appear to exist again when we call them to mind. Holding steadily to the right now eliminates the fear or anxiety that can be associated with thoughts about the future.

By detaching from the past and the future, we can focus on all the wonder of simply being present in our skin right now. This can be as easy as seeing the beauty of the sunrise, a cloud, a tree, a flower, a smile or a painting on the wall. It may be the sound of a baby, a friend, a loved one, a laugh or the wind through the trees. It is easy to appreciate the aroma of delicious food cooking, fresh herbs, flowers or perfume.

These common things oftentimes go unnoticed with concerns about the next minute, the next day, or the next years. Painful thoughts about the past or fear and anxiety about the future can eliminate the present in our consciousness.

In practice as a busy physician, it is easy to lose the moments and many positive aspects of the doctor patient experience. There are many things that hold thoughts like performance pressure, time pressure, and medical record production pressure. While performing a task and a service to patients, it is still very important to enjoy the process. There is always something special in being in the moment with the patient. It is a very privileged opportunity to help and to possibly, significantly impact another person's life. Few professions have an opportunity to have this kind of impact.

Every moment is also an opportunity to utilize the power of our intention. It is possible to change any experience simply with an intention to change it. All our thoughts have the energy and the opportunity for manifesting.

We are the real time creators of our personal plans and have the responsibility and the opportunity to make our intentions. While dreams are inspired from the spirit, the higher self, they are put into motion with the conscious action of intention. There are whispers (and sometimes screams) of our desires for goals that must be turned into plans.

There is immense power in defining intentions. It is the blueprint for manifestation of our dreams and our goals. Daily intentions are a regular part of my routine and I state them before I open my eyes in the morning. These are typically plans for a happy, healthy, productive day but also a personal intention to be present in the moment in the midst of all that I have to do through the day.

In this conversation, in a very important moment, Sonny challenged me. His request gave birth to a new intention. At that time this new goal was daunting. But later, when the time was right, it was clearly meant to be. It was definitely a part of my spiritual life plan.


"Chris, how are you? How is life treating you?"

I'm good Sonny. I am at the end of a really crazy, busy week, but it went well. Everybody is doing well. I took care of a lot of people this week. It was a bit busier than usual. How are you today?

"I am good. Always trying to get to the Atman. Have you heard that term before, Atman?"

Tell me about it.

"I am trying to get to the Atman, to those things that really mean something."

What things are you referring to?

"Have you heard the story about the two birds?

There are two birds. One bird is at the upper part of the tree and he is sitting there serenely. He is regal and calm. The other bird is on the lower part of the tree. He is eating all the fruit that he can get. Some fruits are bitter. Some fruits are sweet. He eats them both going through his life. The other bird is just sitting there calmly on the higher limb in the tree. The lower bird continues to eat the fruit.

This is a metaphor for our human behavior. That is what we do during our lives. We go after gold. We go after fame. We go after sex. We go after money. All of these things. That is a lower bird going through his life. He is satisfying the senses.

The other bird on the higher part of the tree does nothing. The lower bird continues through his life, but his mind becomes more aware of his actions. The actions begin to fall off. As his actions change he notes that he is getting higher and higher on the tree. The upper bird is still as cool as a cucumber at the top of the tree.

The lower bird is wondering what is up with him. Eventually as the lower bird gets closer, he realizes that he IS the other bird on the higher limb. The calm cool bird on the top that was just being there in equanimity not engaging in the many activities of his life is his higher true self. He realizes that the images of himself on the lower limbs are not really him.

The story is an allegory about the human soul. This is man eating the sweet fruit at times and then eating the sour fruit. You can do whatever you want to do but you will deal with the results of your actions. If you want to just eat ice cream, you can. But you will have to deal with the consequences. But if you want to get some wisdom you won't just eat ice cream.

This was me. I finally got it together and found out that I can't just chase the fruit on the lower tree. I want to have the awareness of the top bird."

Great story. The top bird is his true self, his higher self.

"Yes, the top bird is his true self, Atman. That is what we all are. We have to keep progressing to the realization of our true higher self."

That is a great story! We have all of these layers that include the mental and physical as well as the higher spiritual layer. We are multidimensional. Although we may not be aware of our higher spiritual dimension, it is the true and fundamental layer. It is the true self that manifests all physical and mental parts of our expression on earth. The higher bird is the true self. The real self that has no physical needs or attachment. It is the part that was never born and never dies. In the higher levels of consciousness, we recognize a sameness or a unity of all spirits.

"That is the perfection that we want to get to. That is what it is all about. That is what we have to do. We have to learn and to get to that top bird."

I have experienced glimpses of that unity in moments with my patients when I sense that they really hear me and feel my desire to help them to be healthier. This week I had some special moments like this when I was feeling very exhausted. They were like spiritual gifts that inspired me and reminded me of the reason why I do what I do.

"I hope that you are not working too hard. In the airplane they tell you to place the oxygen mask on yourself first and then on your children. If you don't take care of Chris, there will be no-one for your kids and your patients. You've got to take care of yourself."

I hear you Sonny, I'm fine. As you say, It's all good. I am grateful when I am busy. I feel very fortunate to be in a profession where I can really impact people's lives in a good way. I'm also lucky to be able to just open hours and have them fill up very easily.

But I never really expected to have to do the hours that I have now after more than twenty years of practice. Or to have to increase my hours to stay in practice on my own. A lot of people join big groups to share overhead. But I've gotten spoiled by the time that I get to spend with people since I do all my testing personally. This would never happen in a group practice with nurses and technicians. At this point, I don't want to do it any other way.

Besides, I have always felt that the value of my work is in the work itself, not in the money that I get paid to do it. So, by seeing more people I get to help more people. There is a lot more value. It's fine.

"What you are doing is very important. You are doing

what you have been called to do. You are on the right track. You are making a difference in the lives of your patients."

I think that I do make a difference. Since I don't have a nurse or a technician, and since I do all of my testing, I spend a very large amount of time with the patients. In that time, I can feel that there is a change that happens. While they are laying there as I am looking at their hearts on the echo machine, they relax and there is an opening in those moments.

"Of course, there is. They can feel your good energy. They can feel that you want to help them."

I think that they feel something. I sense that they are relaxing. They leave the office with a different calmer energy. That opening allows me to get them to listen to me when I am advising them to do things that will make them healthier. I have an unusual success getting people to stop smoking, to exercise and to eat better. I believe it happens because of that moment of opportunity when they are really listening while feeling my good intentions for them.

"Wow. That's wonderful. They are very fortunate to have you. But you have to take care of yourself too."

I'm fine. Sonny, the same thing applies to you. You have an opportunity with your fans. By that I mean that you have an opening with your fans. They are adoring of you because of your lifetime of music. They have listened to you for years and they have immense affection for you. They have felt your spirit through your music on recordings and in your live performances.

"Well, there is a reason that they listen to my music. There is something that they get. I hope that they feel something, something positive. I want it to be positive. That is what it is all about."

I know that they feel your energy. That is why you should share all your beautiful wisdom with them. They would be open to this kind of knowledge from you when they might not listen to other sources. You have told me many things that have helped me and inspired me. You should share these things with others. You have told me enough things to fill a book. I could write a book with all the things that you have said to me. You should get someone to write it down.

"Well, I could write a book with all the things that you have told me. You write it."

That is an idea. Here with my life, my kids, my practice, my new courses, that is quite a concept. But Sonny, if you like, I would be honored to write it.

"I would like that. But, I won't be involved in it. It will be your writing."

You are involved because it will be your words.

"There are a couple of guys who are writing books now. They have long projects going and have their publishing companies."

A couple. Wow.

"There are always people wanting to write books about me. I try to dissuade them. But, I couldn't do it. This will be different. These people are writing about my music career. Not about my present thoughts or spirituality. What you are talking about are different experiences that I've had that provided me with some gems of wisdom that may be of useful to others."

Exactly. I know that this would be inspiring to many.

"I believe that this may be true because people call me, and they always comment on my spiritual answer to whatever is going on."

Yes. Just like I have done for the past few years.

"So, I know that there is something there. That is what I have been doing for many years. Trying to find out why we are here, and what we are supposed to do while we are here."

It is life wisdom Sonny.

"Well that is all that matters to me now. I'm trying to get understanding about these higher things. About the inner being."

I believe that there is an audience that will benefit from your thoughts.

"Well okay, you know I am at a disadvantage in regard to commenting on my utility. I am learning. Trying to get something."

Well Sonny, you have a life of wisdom that you can share, and it is like anything else that you want to learn. It is far better to open up and listen to those who have years of life experience and use that as a basis rather than starting from the beginning and having to learn it all on your own.

Having an open heart when you learn is very important because when we are talking about these concepts it is not just cognitive. One must at first be open to these things. That is where there are immense benefits with your fans who have a relationship with you already. They start in a place that is a good place to learn.

"I don't know. Maybe you are right. But that is the last thing that I want to think about, myself as being some kind of a seer or a sage for other people. If I am, then fine. But I am quite self-effacing in that way. It would be completely out of character for me to think of myself as having something to offer to people. I am learning myself. I am learning every day."

I understand. But remember how we have talked about the truth. In this case you are just the conduit. You are the mechanism for giving the information. You don't have to take credit for the information itself, but you can be the mechanism. And that is the key, because the information is available in many places. These thoughts are available in many books and lectures. But how do you get people to read it, to listen and to hear it. They have to be open to it, that is the opportunity.

How about just think of it as being a teacher. That is what

you are doing when you are sharing information. You are teaching.

"That's right. Yes, I guess so. I know that my time investigating these matters is not lost because many people tell me that they feel better after talking to me.

But I am not going to dwell on that. I am learning. I am not interested in puffing myself up and thinking about myself. That would short circuit myself and interfere with my process. I am just a human being trying to find out the reason that we are here. How to live well and how to do well. If I can help someone else, then fine."

# Chapter 4

## Glimpsing the Soul

*"I know now.*
*I don't think.*
*I don't believe.*
*I don't hope.*
*I know that,*
*it's all good."*

Miracles are present in our daily lives. There are miracles to see in the beauty of a soaring bird, the magnificence of a rose and the fluttering wings of a hummingbird. The potential of a seed that grows to a tree or a luscious vegetable in the garden is phenomenal. When we stop seeing these things as regular and become aware of their splendor, we enter a space of wonder.

In these moments, we become more aligned with the universal energy and have an opportunity to connect with our higher consciousness. This connection is evident when we experience intuition or "coincidences" in our daily lives. Sometimes there are profound moments in which we are called to a higher understanding or a higher level of being. At these times we become aware of our higher self, our true self, with all the knowledge of our potential and our purpose.

In the last two years I have had many life changing experiences that were moments of glimpsing my higher self. Many experiences led me to developing my practice of meditation and my decision to further my education in the area of natural healing.

The first major meeting that I attended during my cardiology training was the American Heart Association meeting in New Orleans in November of 1989. At this meeting data was presented on the findings that eating a low fat vegetarian diet, exercise, yoga and meditation can reverse atherosclerotic blockages in arteries. I had a personal presentation of this astonishing data because the chief investigator of these studies sat next to me on my flight home.

He was very positive, friendly and energetic and very excited about his studies. His recommendations for lifestyle changes were easy for me to understand and to immediately implement in my personal practice and in my recommendations for my patients. However, the concept of meditation was foreign to me. I knew nothing about this practice. But his findings and strong positive energy ignited a desire in me to learn more. I wanted to recommend it to my patients, but this was difficult because of my limited understanding.

The intention was there, and I tried for over twenty years to learn more about the practice using tapes, books, CD's and online programs. But over this time, I missed the main concept which is moving to silent awareness, away from physical sensations, movement and thoughts to connect with the gap, or the space between our thoughts.

When the first *Oprah and Deepak 21 Day Meditation Experience* was launched, I took advantage of this fantastic tool. These are healing series of guided meditations filled with wisdom and delivered with the beautiful, loving, and calming voices of Oprah Winfrey and Deepak Chopra.

I listened to all of the series and repeated them regularly. I clearly had benefits even though I was not following a primary recommendation which was to sit quietly during the meditation. My daily life was filled with full time cardiology practice and busy mothering of triplets. Multitasking was my constant and I would typically "meditate" by listening to the guided meditation with earphones while cooking dinner, or even more ridiculously, while on my stairmaster or exercising on the floor. I enjoyed listening to the sessions.

Since I participated in the meditation series, I was on an email list for the Chopra Center and received many announcements for events. At one time, I received a notification for a meditation course, Seduction of the Spirit. When I opened the email and read the description I was excited about an opportunity to force myself to learn how to meditate. I needed to go to this course. It was apparent that I would have to be away from my regular life to stop and practice meditation. However, I quickly changed my mind when I read that the program lasted a full week. The thought of making arrangements for childcare for a week for my kids and arranging care for my mother who had recently had a stroke was daunting. Also, the cost was above what I thought I could afford at that time. I quickly closed the note and went on to other messages.

A few days later, I got another email. I recognized it and did not open it. Then, a few days later, I got the email....... again. This time, something different happened. I paused. I stared at it and I felt something. It was an unusual sensation of space in my chest. After a few moments, I opened the note. Already knowing what it said, I stared at it. I wasn't reading it... just blankly looking at the page. I knew. I had to go to this course.

Then my mind kicked in strongly and I thought, no, I can't. It's too much time. I can't afford it now. It's not possible.

Then I had the sensation of space more strongly in my chest. I felt in my heart, in my core, that I had to go to this course.

I gave in a bit, letting go of my negative thoughts and decided to try my credit card with the highest likelihood for success with an intention that if the charges went through, I would just find a way to make it happen.

I was surprised when the charges processed through on a partially full credit card. More than that, I felt excited and happy to go with this flow. I know now that this was probably the best investment that I have ever made, and that the benefits of the program were immense and invaluable.

As the meeting date approached, arrangements for help with my kids and my Mom fell easily into place. But right before the course there was a large amount of preparation. I had to get things settled in the office and prepare for meals, care and activities for the kids. Finally, there was last minute packing.

By the time I got to the retreat, I was exhausted. The momentum that keeps me going day and night at home stopped after I checked in and put my bags down. A couple of days of rest before the course would have been perfect.

I jumped right in to the sessions. I was very excited but continued to be very fatigued. The data that was presented about the benefits of meditation and the natural health benefits of the Perfect Health lifestyle blew my mind.

I was very moved by the gentle, loving, nature of the staff, and the speakers. On the second day, one of the speakers walked around the stage looking at the audience and he walked to the left where I sat and looked right at me. He did this again a few moments later and at that moment, I had a vision of myself as part of teaching these wonderful principles and practices of natural preventative health and healing. I saw myself teaching my patients and wanted to learn everything that I could.

This came to me from somewhere beyond my mind because my thoughts were not in agreement with this plan. I was feeling immensely exhausted and could not imagine adding another task to my bulging agenda. I resisted for a few moments telling myself that this was not possible. However, as my mind was embattled with this new calling, there was a persistent knowingness. It was a desire that I knew was true and there was no benefit to resisting. As soon as I released my grip on the fight going on in my mind I could feel the flow. The next day I signed up for the teacher's certification program. Hoping that it would be as it was before, I looked forward to the details falling into place. And, they did.

My visions and intuition pulled me to my right path and the loving force of the universe placed the stepping stones directly in front of me.

Happy Friday Sonny. How are you today?

"Well, you know, I try to be the same every day. So, I guess that's where I'm at. Some place in the middle."

How do you feel today?

"I feel good. I feel thankful for my time on earth. The good the bad and the ugly. And the, you know, the opportunity to try to be better. To try to improve and to learn something. So, It's all good."

How's the weather up there. Is it freezing cold?

"No, we are still having a mild winter here. How is it in California? "

Well the rain has finally stopped, and we've got beautiful weather.

I've got a couple of classes to teach today. That will be fun. I'm looking forward to the weekend with the kids and my gardening.

"Wow. What energy. I'm happy that you are doing all the things that you want to do. You've got your practice and all the people who depend on you. Your energy is inspiring me today. I can feel it coming through the phone."

Well, I've found that when I am doing things that are creative, the energy and the flow just magnify. The patients have inspired me as I have watched them evolve in my class. The meditators are changing before my eyes. While I've taken care of these people for a while, some for a long time, I have seen changes and an opening. I can see it in their eyes. I can see and feel an opportunity in this realm that is completely different and full of potential. It is making me feel very blessed to be a part of it with them. I am also getting confirmation in their eyes that I am exactly where I am supposed to be right now. I am on my path my dear.

"It is so great and vast, this consciousness. It's so fantastic. There's so much more then we can understand as humans. We have a little bit of knowledge, but it is very vast beyond our understanding. The big picture indeed. I have been up to the same thing. Trying to learn, to live and learn. Maintain some kind of enlightenment...... You know."

When you say vast it makes me think of how big it all can be. I have noticed that as soon as I have fulfilled a goal and gotten to the point that things are rolling in one goal, I am inspired, and another plan just opens up. At this point I have learned to not worry about it. In the past I used to feel overwhelmed when I glimpsed a goal because I was already at what I perceived to be full capacity. When I first was inspired to be a teacher I was pretty intimidated by the thought of doing more. I wondered how in the world would I fit this in to my present schedule. It made me feel uncomfortable and a bit nervous.

Luckily, I followed my intuition and started the process. Then it just unfolded for me. Now I've gotten to the point where I can be more creative and go with the flow. I can look forward to the future knowing that it will fall in place for me.

I just have to stay with my intention and move with my inspiration. I don't have to figure it all out right now. I can think, okay, I see that in my future and then let it go.

"It is very important for you to bring that teaching to people. Natural healing methods and preventative medicine are wonderful. I am very proud of you."

What's going on with all your interviews. Do you have anything coming up?

"Well, ha, ha, ha, ha.... I was doing so many of these interviews. I have finally gotten to the point where I don't feel that I want to be on camera. I've been doing them because people get a lot out of them, but it takes a lot out of me."

Well follow your intuition and if you want to do it, do it and if you don't, don't. Ask yourself, not in your head but in your heart. If you want to do it, you should do it. If it is something you are meant to do, you will feel a definite calling to do it. If you are not, and you don't want to do it, I can't imagine why you would.

"Yeah it's that simple. It really is."

Maybe you get called to do something and initially you don't think that you want to do it but then you feel a strong pull or a calling for it. You can feel it. Get out of your head and feel it in your heart. Your intuition makes you feel that you need to do it. It can be hard to know what to do but I think the only time that we make mistakes is when we don't follow that calling or feeling, that gut feeling, that intuition. I think it's the calling of our spirit to do what we need to do. You have done so many wonderful programs and I am sure that every time that you do one, someone receives some benefit. But you have to be able to pick and choose the ones to do.

"Yes. And it takes a lot out of me. So, it's a matter of what will it produce. Will it produce enough benefit for somebody else such that it is worth it. So that is a big part at this stage of my life."

How much control do you have over the situation? I know you told me once that you agreed to a certain amount of time and they went way over it. Is that a frequent problem?

"They always go over it. Everybody always wants more time. But, anyway, at this stage in my life that is the least that I am thinking about. How much it will help other people, okay, that is something that I will think about. But I don't need any more publicity or anything like that."

Do you see the finished products, the videos?

"No. I don't."

That's not right. I would think that they would give you a copy of anything that you are in. It's not standard for them to send you a copy?

"It's not standard for me because I don't have the means of viewing it here. I can get a copy if I want one. That is not a problem."

So, all the things that you have done, you have never seen the interviews?

"No. Most of them, I have not. But it's no problem, It's all good. It's just the way that I wanted it to be."

Well, I know that you are not really in to looking at yourself. Right?

"Right! Right. That is correct."

I want to see them.

"That is what I mean, it will be available to other people."

"How is Les. How is your Dad doing?"

He is doing great. He is meditating.

"Still in New Orleans?"

Yes. He won't go back to Paris till the spring. He just told me a story about you. He told me that one time when he went to see you play, he went back stage to visit with you. When he asked a band member about where you were, they pointed to a closet. He opened the closet door and found you there meditating with your horn.

"Ha, ha, ha, ha...."

This was before your performance. Does that sound familiar?

"Sure. At times that was my routine. That is sort of normal for me."

I hope that he didn't disturb you. (Laughs)

"No, no, no. I wasn't in that deeply in that environment. That was not intense meditation. It was a meditation in more hectic circumstances."

Maybe just a moment of awareness or some space, or air before you went on?

"Yes, that was a routine for me before I performed.

But I have had other more profound moments of awareness that are far beyond this body and this mind. Moments that changed my life.

A very powerful incident happened in the middle of my tour many years ago. I was in the middle of the countryside in France. I was there for a performance in Marciac. It's in the part of France heading toward Spain. I stayed in a very nice hotel…. but it's in the countryside, not a big hotel. I was preparing for my performance that night and had to find my dental partial. I was looking for it because I need to wear it in order to play my horn.

I searched everywhere in the small room. I looked on the tables, on the floor, everywhere in the room. I searched and searched again and could not find it. I did not find it. I was panicked. I told the hotel people about the partial. They were looking through the things they had taken from my room. They were very nice and certainly understood my panic, but they could not find it.

I kept searching and searching. I was in a point of despair, then, I looked up. There in my hotel room, I saw a vision of the sky. In the sky, I saw a window that opened side to side, vertically. not horizontally. It was opened just the slightest. Just a bit, an inch opening. I looked up and could see through this opening. And I saw a vision of what was behind. I saw beyond everything that existed in this world. I saw a more beautiful place. I saw that there was much more than what we see here.

I had a glimpse of what was there beyond what we are able to see. At that moment I knew this was something. It was really something powerful and beautiful. I immediately felt completely enriched. I felt out of this world. After that I was bursting with consciousness. What I had seen was so far beyond this world. I was in a place that I had never been. For a long time, the enormity of this left me feeling like I was bursting out of my skin. I was in a zone. I was in seventh heaven. I told everyone that I could about it. It changed everything for me."

What did you see?

"There are no words."

What did you feel?

"I felt elated, enlightened. It was far more beautiful than anything I could imagine here."

Do you think that it was a window into your higher self, your true self?

"I don't know what it was behind the window. But it was all good. 'It is all good,' is an understatement. It was a fantastic experience, far beyond anything that I had experienced before. I was glimpsing my soul."

Did that experience change your thinking in any way?

"Well, I wouldn't say that it changed my thinking, it confirmed my thinking. It confirmed everything."

When was this Sonny?

"It was about seven, eight years ago. I try to think back on that when I get enmeshed in this little world. I know that a little lesson came to me. I don't talk about it much now, but for months, I talked about it to different people. Around the time that it happened I couldn't contain it. I don't want to use the word, joy, that is too small of a word. It was a high vibration that I felt, and it was sort of beating out of me. I could not contain it. It was one of the most beautiful moments of my life."

You glimpsed your soul? The universe?

"One would think so. At that moment, something opened up. The window opened up just a little bit, and boy, what an experience. I have had a lot of wonderful things that have happened but that was the most dramatic and profound.

After the vision, I didn't worry about the partial. I did not care about this world. I knew that whatever happened, it didn't matter. I was in a place that I had never experienced. But shortly thereafter, I found the partial there under the chair where I had looked before. I know I had looked there. It wasn't a big room.

It was as if it had all happened for a reason. It was like a personal trick to show me the true reality. I realized that if I did not find my partial that it did not matter.

I know now. I don't think. I don't believe. I don't hope. I know that, it's all good."

# Chapter 5

# Synchronicity

*"There is only one truth.*
*There are not a million truths.*
*Everyplace you go, another truth.*
*There's a truth in India.*
*There's a truth in Japan.*
*There's a truth in Hong Kong.*
*There's a truth in London.*
*No, no, there is only one truth."*

If we are aware or conscious in our daily life, we can benefit from an open connection with our spirit which provides us with tools in the form of intuition, hunches, desires, and clear signs or confirmations that we are on the right path.

Our deepest desires are forces from our spirit that are guiding us toward a certain path. If we follow these deep desires, we won't make mistakes or poor decisions. If we go with the flow that is directed by our spirit, we are following our path. Even if the path appears to be rocky or filled with obstacles, our path has a reason, a very powerful valuable reason.

Things happen frequently that give us confirmation that we are heading in the right direction. If we recognize these things, it makes it easier to know that we are on the right path. This happened when I had my first call with Sonny. I was reading a book and stopped at a paragraph to call him. Shortly into our first conversation Sonny said the exact words that I had just read in the book.

This is called synchronicity and it happens to everyone. You may have a thought about someone and then they call you on the phone or send you a message shortly thereafter. You may have a thought or a question on your mind and then you find the words or the answer in a book, on a billboard or a magazine cover. You may think of something, a movie, a person, a book, that you have not thought of for a long time and then find this particular thing surprisingly in your environment. The perfect solution to a problem may appear at exactly the right time.

These wonderful happenings are your higher self, your spirit tapping you gently on the shoulder, and saying to you,

"I am here, you are on the right track. Full force ahead." These synchronous happenings are also strong forces that change the course of our lives.

My gardening has evolved from flowers and herbs to vegetables and fruit. We had wonderful produce in the summer of 2014 and I did my usual harvesting. But in the winter, I spent no time with vegetables. On Saturday, January 17, 2015, we had an unusually warm day. The weather was beautiful, and the kids and I were having fun in the backyard. They were playing, and I was joyously working in my garden beds.

When I got around to one corner, I was shocked to find a large shiny eggplant. It had grown through the winter without any notice or care from me. I would typically spend the whole Saturday out in the garden enjoying the weather. But the existence of this eggplant was a miracle that I wanted to share with my mother. I brought it into the house with plans to show it to her. When I walked in she was in the bathroom, so I put it on the table and headed back out to the garden.

Shortly after getting back into my pleasurable work, I had another strong desire to show the eggplant to my mother. So, I took off my gloves, went back inside, grabbed the eggplant from the table and headed downstairs to my mother's room.

When I got to her bedroom door, I immediately knew that something was terribly wrong. She was lying diagonally across her bed staring up at the ceiling. I rushed in and pulled her up. She was very confused complaining of a headache. Her speech was slurred, and her entire left side was not moving.

I recognized a major stroke in progress and immediately called 911. I called for a friend to watch the kids and left for the hospital shortly after she left in an ambulance.

Since I knew that she had been in the bathroom just minutes before, we were able to accurately time the onset of her stroke. The timing of a stroke is crucial in order to determine if a patient is eligible for a clot busting medication which must be given within a few hours of the onset of symptoms. If it is given within a window of 3-4.5 hours, some people can have marked improvement and a reversal of some of the damage from the stroke. She was well within this therapeutic window and got the medication.

She received efficient, kind and loving urgent care in the emergency room. The nurses and physicians were superb and worked with concern and a high level of skill. We all watched with strong intentions and with anticipation, hoping to see any sign of improvement. I would frequently direct her to move her toes or her fingers. At the same time, I told her that she was going to be fine and to keep looking at me. I smiled at her with strong intentions. I knew that she was afraid, and I wanted her to be hopeful. Many attempts at movement were unsuccessful. After some intensely stressful hours with a waiting room filled with family and many other's praying in multiple states, there was a glorious small response to my direction. At first, there was very small movement in her foot. Then her left sided paralysis miraculously began to resolve and she was able to move her toes, foot and fingers. It was breathtaking.

The eggplant was a gift that was presented to me at just the right time. When I first went into the house my mother was up and walking but not available to see my eggplant. About a half hour later she was in her bed having a life-threatening stroke. I had a strong desire to show my mother the eggplant not once, but two times. The timing of both visits into the house were crucial.

I would have typically been outside for many hours on a Saturday. If the stroke had happened on any day of the week, I would have been at work. The synchronicity of finding the eggplant and my desire to show it to my mother saved her life.

Synchronous events have occurred many times during my conversations with Sonny. There were several instances in which I got confirmation that talking to Sonny and writing this book were a part of my plan. Sonny reasserted this for me when we talked about his wife, Lucille.

Sonny, you sound tired, are you okay?

"Well I've been on the phone all day dealing with some things. It doesn't matter. It's all good.

You know on this planet we have to deal with things. But as human beings we don't understand everything. We are lucky to understand a few things. If it is happening, it's happening for a good reason. We might be feeling that it's a terrible thing but even if it's death, or so-called death, that is a part of life. Things can appear to be really bad. But, we have to realize that it is all part of a plan. It's hard to do this when we are in the middle of it. I'm just in the middle of something that I have to deal with. On this earth we have to deal with many things. I'm just going through my thing right now. That's a long answer to your question, am I alright."

I don't like that you are going through something difficult. I'm sorry about that.

"It's okay. It's my karma I have to deal with. Someday I will understand why things happen the way they did on earth. It's part of my journey. Don't be sorry, be happy."

I'm very happy. I'm doing my studying for my certification. Soon I'll be going back down to the Chopra Center for my final training. I am learning about Vedanta, the core of the teachings from the center. This ancient enlightened wisdom and philosophy predates all religion. In my classes and studies, I've been reading and hearing many of the things that you've been telling me for years.

"Well look. Please remember, there is only one truth. There are not a million truths. Everyplace you go there is another truth. There's a truth in India. There's a truth in Japan. There's a truth in Hong Kong. There's a truth in London. No, no. There is only one truth.

How is everyone? How is your Dad?"

I just talked to my Dad last night. He talked about you a lot. He was recalling the moment that he met you. He also told me a funny story about the first time that you saw him and his twin brother together. He said that you had seen them both separately for many years, but they were together at your performance in Nice. He said that you told them that after finally seeing them together, you were no longer suspicious that they had been pulling your leg making believe that they were two people.

"Ha, ha, ha, ha.... I remember that. I was in Nice with my wife Lucille."

That is interesting that you bring up your wife. Dad was talking about her last night. Her presence must be around now.

"Of course, she is around. As a matter of fact, that is funny that you said that. I took Lucille to India many times. A friend of mine from India just sent me a picture that he took at my house in 1972 in Brooklyn. I was with Lucille and his family in the picture. I just got that today. So, you see, you said Lucille must be around. Well, she definitely is around."

Wow, Dad mentioned her. Your friend just sent you a picture of her. She must be abruptly around. Tell me about her. Sadly, I didn't get to meet her.

"She was a very brilliant woman. We were together for forty years. We had one period where we separated for a little while, but we got back together. We lived together in Germantown for forty years. We traveled the world together. She traveled on tour with me. She took care of my business for me. She loved the music business, so I was able to allow her to take care of all of my business. She kept things in good stead."

Sounds like a perfect match. How did you meet? How did you find her?

"Well, she found me. I was playing in Chicago. She was from Kansas City, but she was living in Chicago at the time. She saw me performing and said to herself, that's the guy for me. She told me that later. So that's it. She had me in eyesight and she came to New York."

How did she go from wanting to meet you to meeting you?

"She knew the wife of one of the guys in the band and told her that she really wanted to meet me. The guy told me, and we met and had a nice relationship. She moved to New York and we got married. Then unfortunately......not unfortunately, she lived her life and did great things with me. She helped me enormously.

Lucille was Caucasian, by the way. They wouldn't let me do what I wanted to do with my music career. So, I told her look, this is what I want to do, and this is what I need to do. I schooled her on what the score was.

She used to work at The University of Chicago. She worked for a professor in the physics laboratory. Lucille being the real deal when it comes to Americana, these guys that she had to deal with in the music business had to acquiesce to her. So, there were things that I wanted that she was able to get for us."

That's fantastic. So, she traveled and worked with you.

"Yes, we traveled all over the world together. She was my personal manager. We were in Nice when we met up with Lowell and your father. That is why they all know her."

I'm sorry that I did not get to meet her.

"Well, you were too young at that time.

After she had a stroke, Lucille did not want to go to the hospital. I took care of her at home in the last period of her life before she transitioned.

I know that she is around. After Lucille passed away, about a week later, I saw her in the house. It was in my living room. We looked at each other and went through a whole lifetime of things. Just by looking at each other. I don't believe in death as people do. I know spirits come back. I was not surprised. I was glad that she came and that I saw her so that we had that sort of meeting."

Have you had any other experiences like that since she died?

"Not like that. Not her image. But her spirit, yes. She came to me once in a dream. There was a woman that I met in Hudson New York. She was shopping at the health food store. We became friends and we were talking on the phone.

I have two kinds of dreams. The unreal dream and then the real dream. I was thinking about getting closer to this woman. One night while I was sleeping, Lucille came to me in a real dream and she told me, no! No! No!"

Did she say why?

"No, she did not say why but she knew something. I had to accept what she said. I am not in a position to question her."

Wow. (Laughs). That's funny.

"It is funny isn't it. Ha, ha, ha, ha…."

You wonder was there something wrong there.

"Maybe there would have been some kind of problem with that possible relationship. From her spiritual vantage point, apparently, she saw something. That is how I took it. That is why I tell you all the time that when you are in another realm you can see things differently. In time I might realize why that happened."

That is a great thing to have. An advisor from beyond who has your absolute best interest at heart. She intervened.

"Ha, ha, ha, ha…."

It's interesting. I wonder what is going on cosmically right now because she came up in my conversation with Dad. And then, in our conversation. I have to say that is the first time you have both spoken to me about Lucille. It happened within hours of each other.

"Not only that, I just got these pictures of her from this guy. The pictures are back from 1972. That shows that there is an intelligence that is present that we cannot see. Things are happening for a reason. It's not just random. There is a hand that is writing. There is a reason that things go on."

You know there was something else that Dad said to me about her. He said that he remembered talking to you about the bridge and that you told him that Lucille was a major part of your being able to be on the bridge.

"That's correct. That was 1959. I decided to take a hiatus and do some remedial musical work that I felt I needed to do to justify people coming to see me.

I always was a guy who loved to practice. Practicing was my life. Wherever I was, I wanted to find someplace to practice. Living in New York it's hard to practice because the apartment buildings were right next to each other. If you practice you're going to disturb somebody. All musicians have that problem.

The bridge was just a few blocks from where I lived. One day I was walking and saw a path, walked up some steps and found a place where I could practice. I would find a place where I would not be seen by people, by the trains or the cars.

When I was on the bridge I didn't have a whole gang of money. But Lucille was living with me at that time. She had a very nice job working for a professor at New York University. She worked all that time while I was on the bridge.

After I came off of the bridge, she wanted to learn about the business. I schooled her about it. I took her to my recording sessions and got her acquainted with what she would have to do. I knew what I needed to have done but I could not do it. They would not let a black jazz musician do it. I had tried, but I realized that I could not do what I wanted and needed to do. They could not deny her because her intellect was greater than theirs."

So, she was a crucial part of your being able to do your music the way that you wanted to do it.

"Yes. It's all crucial. We were married for forty years."

I am sorry that I did not get to meet her.

"Well you met her now. You got to hear all about her. I am glad you got a chance to meet Lucille. It's all good. Life goes on. I am trying to learn and trying to get better every day. I am eternally grateful that each day I have another chance to try to get it right."

Do you feel like your knowledge is opening up in the last few years? Do you feel you are more in touch with your true self?

"Oh sure. I know I feel I am learning a lot. I've been on a more positive path for quite a while now. Even with being on this path I still have a lot to learn. This is the beauty of life----how many things there are to learn. It's just so fantastic and divine. It is vast and never ending."

Like running up a hill and seeing what you could not see before and then running over that hill to another hill and seeing beyond that hill. An unending journey of new experiences.

"That is very true. I recently heard that the further back you are the more you can see in front of you. This is another little thing that happens to me that I have observed. It's like ringing a bell. What you just said is something that I have recently thought about. This is confirmation."

Yes. synchronicity, confirmation.

"It's always nice to have my mind in a still enough place that I can observe these things happening."

Those things are fun to me. I think they're like your spirit letting you know you are right were you should be. Do you remember when that happened in our first conversation? I was reading a book and you said something that was exactly what I had just read before I got on the phone with you.

"Yes. I do remember that."

That was my spirit telling me keep calling Sonny! (Laughs). Our calls were important. My spirit was tapping me and telling me that this is the path for you. Stay on it.

"Thank you very much for that. Those little clues that come to us in life are really wonderful. They let you know, hey you are on the right track."

Chapter 6

# Inspirations

*"You can't mess over others and think that it's okay.*
*It is not okay. It will come back to you.*
*Once you realize that you start doing right.*
*I came into this world having an understanding of*
*that."*

Inspirations are very powerful. I was very fortunate as a child to be advised by my parents that there were no limitations on my personal life goals. My father encouraged me at a very young age that I could do anything that I wanted to do. My mother strongly encouraged me to be sure to take care of my education and to empower myself so that I could rely on myself for all that I wanted in life.

My father's method of impressing upon me my limitless possibilities was the same that he taught my brothers. He did not consider, apply or even address any difference in regard to gender. I had five brothers and felt that we all had the same opportunity and capability. When I first encountered blatant sexism in medical school, I was puzzled by it and immediately thought that there was clearly something wrong with the holders of these ridiculous thoughts and judgments. It was too silly to me to think that people could be labeled and categorized based on their gender or race. And, importantly, no matter what they thought, I knew that I could do anything that I wanted to do.

People are often shocked when I tell them that during medical school, I was told twice by my attending staff physicians that, "Women should not be doctors." The first time was in my first clinical rotation during open heart surgery. I was assisting on a coronary bypass procedure, when a world-famous heart surgeon told me in front of the entire surgical crew, "Christy, I just have to tell you that, I don't believe women should be doctors." First of all, this was not my name, since I was referred to as Chris or Christine. Secondly, the patient's chest was open, and I was actively assisting in this surgery. My job was to hold the patient's heart up while the surgeon sewed on his distal coronary bypass grafts.

This was an irresponsible and dangerous time to be mean to me and I thought that this was a bizarre and ridiculous thing to say. I did not respond verbally but looked at him like he was an idiot. I couldn't help but look at him like he was a clown that did not belong with his hands on the heart of our patient. He could not see my face because I was wearing a surgical mask. I wish now that I had stood up for myself for the benefit of the other women in the room.

The second time was a year later, and I responded better. I was at the end of my intensive care unit rotation with my fellow male students, male interns, male residents and male fellows, when my pulmonary attending told me, "You did a good job on this rotation and I'm going to have to give you an A, but I want you to know that I don't think women should be doctors." All of my male colleagues were aghast. They froze and looked at me with grave concern. Without hesitation, I told him that I believed that I had done an excellent job, that I deserved the A and that I was fortunate that his opinion about women in medicine did not matter to me at all.

I had another bad experience when after rounds at the community hospital, one of my internal medicine attending physicians asked me to give him a table dance. I was very young and naive and had no idea what a table dance was. My fellow male students started shaking their heads strongly, no, no, no. This let me know that it was something terrible. They explained it to me later that he was asking me to dance for him like a stripper would at a table in a strip club. If I had known what he was requesting, I hope that I would have remained calm and not taken it personally. Today after decades of training on these situations, I would easily and calmly tell him that he was abusing his role as my teacher and that it was unacceptable.

People who are fortunate to be in roles as a teachers, counselors or leaders have a real responsibility to lead and to model. Even more than this, they can inspire. Conversely, if they don't positively model and direct in a constructive way they can have immensely negative impacts. One of my patient's dreams to be a psychologist were squashed by a school counselor who told her that this was not a good idea. She continues to regret the loss of her life goal and the negative impact that this counselor had on her. There were many instances in which my female colleagues did not respond well to sexist abuse. I was lucky to be unusually empowered by my home environment.

Fortunately, I grew up with five brothers and I knew that I was capable. It was a training camp in which it became natural for me to hang out with the boys. I could do and did do everything that they did. My father had not made an issue of my sex. It was not an issue for me and I was unusually tough. During my education, I did not take these remarks personally and I found confidence in the quality of my work which they could not dispute.

While these negative comments passed by me like the sound of a passing car disappearing into nothing, I was highly impacted and inspired when I worked with physicians who were brilliant, respectful, nice, and confident but not arrogant. I was impressed by them and wanted to be like them. I remember working in a physician's dictation room in the hospital with a female cardiology fellow in training. I listened to her confidently, quickly, and succinctly dictate a history and physical. I intended to be just like her.

Intentions are crucial to accomplish our life goals and people who inspire us facilitate our ability to see ourselves doing what we want to do in our future. I had many goals and have chosen the role models that were in alignment with the plans that I had for my future. At the same time, I ignored the negative people who wanted to thwart my dreams. Sonny was highly inspired at a very young age by many talented people.

"Happy Labor Day, Chris. It's Labor Day weekend. Are you getting ready to chill some? I hope you are."

No. I'm studying and getting ready for my trip. I'm heading down to the Chopra Center to complete my certification. But, it's still a vacation for me Sonny. When I am learning, being still in a classroom, and absorbing information, that is like a vacation.

"Of course it's a vacation. But only someone of your position in life can appreciate that. Well said."

I am looking forward to it. It is going to be fun. I will be learning the substance of the ayurvedic lifestyle. It involves a lot of the things that we have discussed like meditation, the power of your thoughts, and use of food and your senses for healing. These are concepts that my western medical education ignored. In regard to the power of your thoughts and intentions, I have a lot of experiences that will help me to teach.

"In a way, it's already prescribed for your life. But also, in a way it is not. People say, 'Oh well, it's fate.' No, you have the power to change your karma. You are right on track."

I feel that you are right Sonny. I believe that the way you get off of the right track is by not listening to your intuition. By not following your calling, your spirit which directs you to what you should be doing. Most people would not have taken this on while being as busy as I am. But, I felt a very strong calling for it.

"For you it is what you are supposed to do."

I feel like I am in the flow. Even though it is more work. It feels easy. Not doing it would not feel good. It would not feel right. What are you doing for Labor Day?

"I am going to rest today. Been dealing with some problems that have tired me out. So, I am going to just chill. I am almost done with it. I just have to stay on top of things and then can get it done. It is the sort of thing that we have to go through in life. That's what we are here for to go through stuff and to come out on top."

After we talked last time and you told me about Lucille's presence in your life after she died. I thought of another story you told me some time ago about Clifford Brown.

"Oh yes. We were very close musically. We were the same age. He was a great spirit and influenced my life. He never used drugs. He was a straight guy. Since I had used drugs he really influenced me a lot in a good way. I wasn't using drugs then, but I wasn't straight on other things in the Jazz musician lifestyle. It was really tragic. He was very young and died in a car accident. After he left this place, I used to channel him. I used to call on him and felt that we communicated in my music. After a while I thought that he was on his own journey, his celestial journey and I did not need to bother him.

Just like any family members that have passed. They can always be there for you if you call on them. But we have to let them go on their journey. He's got bigger worlds to go to now."

I also wanted to ask you about Sugar Hill. I have heard you refer to it and wondered if this was where you lived.

"No. I lived in Harlem. Sugar Hill was the high cotton. Harlem was not. Sugar Hill was where all the top black people in our community lived. Like W. E. B. Du Bois and Thurgood Marshall.

Great musicians lived in Sugar Hill. We saw them, but we did not hang out with them. Duke Ellington, Coleman Hawkins, lived there. I was a boy, but they lived not far from me."

Did you have an opportunity to see them play when you were young?

"I saw them play as soon as I was old enough to go into clubs to see them. But I saw Duke Ellington in movies. I saw Coleman Hawkins and the guys on 52$^{nd}$ street. I put eyebrow pencil under my nose to make it look like I had a moustache. I don't know if the guys didn't care and just wanted the money, but anyway it worked. "Ha, ha, ha, ha...."

(Laughs) That's funny. I can't imagine that really working.

What do you think inspired you to play the sax? How young were you?

"When I first started to play, I was living in Harlem, not Sugar Hill. I got interested in Jazz early on because I realized the force that Jazz music is.

The great Fats Waller made me see this. He was a guy who was like a comedian in a way. He was a great musician but when he played he would do a lot to make people laugh.

Oh man, he was too much. There was a lot of music in Harlem when I grew up. There was music all over the place.

Clubs in every place. And we heard these guys on the radio. I saw the great Louis Armstrong in movies. When you saw him in a drab movie, all of the sudden, the sun came out."

He had beautiful energy.

"He lifted the picture up. The great Louis Armstrong. I remember the picture I saw with the Nicholas Brothers. They came on the screen in all-white pictures and the whole theater would light up. It was a beautiful thing to see. But that's where I got my inspiration. I listened to Louis Jordan."

When did you get your first horn?

"My uncle got me my first horn when I was seven. He played the saxophone. My mother told him that I wanted to play saxophone and he got me a horn."

Wow. At seven could you hold that saxophone?

"Yes. When I got that saxophone, I went in the room and closed the door. I played, and played, and played. My mother had to come in the room and say, 'Hey Sonny, get out of there, it's time to eat dinner.' I was in heaven."

It was meant to be.

"Yes. It was meant to be."

So, you started playing it on your own without any lessons?

"Oh yes. I played it at first without lessons. I got the horn and I played. Eventually I got lessons. But I wish I had a tape of playing my horn when I played my horn for the first time."

I wish I had a tape of that too. That would be interesting.

"It would be very interesting."

So, was it like magic? Were you able to automatically get sound out of that sax?

"Ha, ha, ha, ha…. Well, you know, I had heard people. I had heard Fats Waller. I had heard Louis Armstrong. As a kid, I had heard all this music. When I first got that horn, I wonder what I played. It was not like I had dropped on this earth from outer space because I had heard stuff. Ha, ha, ha, ha…."

Well it's like what you said about me. You followed your inspiration. You were meant to play that horn and you knew it at a young age.

"There is a reason for everything in life. Things don't happen randomly. There is a reason that this happened. You can say that there is a reason and that this is what you are supposed to be doing. You have to do the right thing, you've got to live like that. You can't mess over others and think that it is okay. It's not okay.

There is a thing called karma and it will come back to you. What goes around comes around. It will come back to you.

So, once you realize that you start living right. You know, not doing bad things to other people.

Some people don't realize that in this lifetime, and they may have to live another lifetime to figure that out. Maybe many lifetimes.

But I am happy to say that I realize that, and I came into this world having an understanding of that. I am trying to go towards the light. Like the Buddhist say, that light of complete understanding. That light of your higher self. You are not your body. Your body is transient. It will stay on this earth, but you will not."

# Chapter 7

# Struggle

*"Life is a struggle. We have to struggle.*
*That is why we are here, to fight the good fight.*
*We are here to learn.*
*Why else would we be here?*
*To have a good time?*
*No, we are here to fight, and to try to get*
*enlightenment, learn something."*

Love is the most powerful force in our universe. The energy of love is immediately transforming. The simple recall of the sensation of love brings lifting energy to our spirits and to our minds. This energy is tangible and infectious.

I have learned about the power and the force of this concept. Oftentimes when a patient is advised by their family doctor that they have symptoms or findings that are concerning enough that they must have a cardiac evaluation, they come to me with a great amount of stress and anxiety. Sometimes that stress and anxiety is manifested or displayed as hostility and anger.

I understand this and have learned that these are the people that may need my help the most. However, it is difficult to try to help a person who is acting angrily. They may come into my office with a loud, irritable, demanding or judgmental tone.

The normal response to this is to withdraw or get angry at them. But this is of no value. When a person is highly emotionally charged on arrival, I am aware of their presence in my small office before I see them because I can hear their negative tone and I can feel their negative energy.

When I was in training I was given names of patients that I had to evaluate and present to my attending physicians or upper-level training staff. I had no choice about whether I would evaluate or treat a patient. I had to see them. Once when I was just starting my cardiology fellowship training, I went to see an elderly, country, Texas man. I opened the door to his hospital room and introduced myself. I was a young physician with my board certification in Internal Medicine, so I appropriately introduced myself as doctor. I was two steps into the room when this man yelled, "Get the hell out of here. You're not a doctor."

I was both shocked and challenged by this. In that quick moment I realized that this history and physical was going to be hard and that in order to get it done, I was going to have to figure out a way to deal with this loud, grumpy, old man.

I hesitated for a short moment at the door and then charged full speed on toward him. My intuition advised to try to "kill him with kindness" and of course, no fear. I softened my voice and explained nicely that I was actually a fully credentialed doctor and that I was working with his heart doctor. I kindly but assertively told him that he had to allow me to do a history and physical in order for him to get his procedure done that day.

He was not happy about this and continued to be mean to me. He insulted the way that I was dressed and told me that I was too young to be a doctor. I ignored him and softly asked him questions about his history.

He answered the questions with displeasure. I kept on with my assertive but pleasant tone and proceeded with his physical.

Towards the end of his exam, he started to relax and unwind before me. I tried not to make eye contact because I didn't want to stop this process. It was working.

When I completed his exam, I sat down next to him and looked at him. His eyes had softened. I started to explain the procedure that we planned. I described the prep of his leg area with plans to place catheters up to his heart using an X-ray machine. I told him that we would use an anesthetic that would only burn a bit and that the procedure would not be very painful. I calmly described our plan to take pictures of the arteries that feed his heart muscle with blood and that we were looking for blockages in these arteries that may be causing his chest pain. If we found a blockage, we planned to fix that blockage at that time with a balloon procedure.

The look in his eyes changed to a vulnerable concern. I touched his arm and told him that he was in good hands and that his physician was highly skilled. I told him the actual risk of the procedure and that I thought that he would do very well. His eyes got full and he thanked me. Then he apologized for treating me the way that he had. I minimized it and assured him that it was okay.

I learned that day about fear dressed up like hostility, anger and aggression. Since then I grew confident in my ability to take care of anyone, no matter how they presented to me. It's easy to take care of nice and happy people. The others are much more of a challenge. I appreciated that they possibly needed my help more. As long as my intention is to help them, they eventually feel it and drop the negative affect and tone.

As my experience has progressed I have found that this process moves much more quickly and easily when I prepare for these patients. When I note the negative angry tone, I start to focus on love and compassion before I see the patient. I bring my attention to my heart and think of the words love and compassion. I focus and repeat this silently before I meet the patient.

This practice has made it much easier for me. I don't sense their negative energy as strongly and they evolve to my energy much more readily. It is hard to stay in fear and hostility when you feel the love of another. It is transforming and healing.

How are you today Sonny?

"I try to stay the same. You know that's what we do when we are on the spiritual path. We watch what's going on, but we do not get involved. We can observe it all but don't get pulled in to it. We can be here but be unattached."

That can be hard to do. I am working on exactly that. My studying helps to keep my mind fully occupied.

"Tell me what exactly are you studying? What will you be teaching?"

I am going to teach a course called Perfect Health. It's based on the principles of Ayurveda which is a 5000-year-old system of preventative health and focuses on treating the mind, the body and the spirit. The course that I will be teaching includes meditation, the use of food and natural senses for healing, and detoxification, movement with yoga,

It's All Good Colossal Conversations with Sonny Rollins

emotional clearing, and conscious communication skills. Right now, I am learning about the primary principles of Ayurveda. This identifies specific mind body types and then particular natural things that can be used to promote healing and maintain health. We teach about the use of clean food for healing and utilizing our senses to treat symptoms that rise from imbalances. This treatment is natural, harmless and very effective.

"I am familiar with Ayurveda and I believe it is pronounced, Ay- ur- ve-da."

Thanks for that correction.

I'm having a good time learning the principles in detail. When I was in medical school, it was always easier for me to understand symptoms, diagnoses and therapy if I understood the physiology behind them. In my clinical years, we had regular rounds with our attending physician staff. My favorite question was, "Why did you say that?" or, "Why did you make that conclusion?" I also liked, "Why do you think this particular choice compared to an alternative, is the best in this situation?"

"Those are good questions."

Yes, they helped me to learn. Once I understood the source of their conclusions, I could understand their reasoning and come to my own conclusion about their comments. So, I am getting into the basis for the Ayurvedic principles. It is a system of health that has as its basis the fact that all things in

84

nature or comprised of a combination of elements. These are space, air, fire, water, and earth. Clearly all things that are manifested in our world are made from these elements. Utilizing these concepts we can determine a person's specific mind or body type and imbalances that lead to symptoms. Then we can make specific recommendations for therapy utilizing particular foods, flavors, aromas, massage, sounds, and colors. It is fascinating and all-natural healing. Most importantly, there are no pharmaceutical side effects.

"Right. That is important."

I am also learning about the value of detoxification which is a concept that I never really thought much about. It is very important to avoid toxins in food and in the environment. When I say environment, I mean everything that we eat, breath, see, hear, and think. I am learning about how toxic our food can be in this country. The use of harmful pesticides is poorly controlled. Our food can be poison. I've said that for years about salt, now I have to broaden my scope to include foods listed by Environmental Working Group as the "Dirty Dozen." After the summary of the report was presented in this course I looked up the report to investigate more. They reported on samples of our food tested by the Department of Agriculture. In their report this year the highlights were a single grape sample and sweet bell pepper sample that contained 15 pesticides. Samples of strawberries showed 17 different pesticides. The results are shocking. It is worth the investment to buy organic when you are buying produce that is on the dirty dozen list. The cheaper stuff is poisonous.

At the end of this course I will be a Certified Chopra Instructor. I will be teaching my patients these principles of natural healing and detoxification. So, I will have a great mix of my traditional western medicine and now Ayurveda which is the foundation of eastern medicine and alternative medicine.

"That's great to hear. Well, we need the east, the west, and the north, and the south. Ha, ha, ha, ha…. It all makes our world, so we need it all.

How is your mother? Is she still on her new routine, doing what she needs to do?"

Remember when I told you that I was happy that she had been able to get on a plane and travel to Vegas for my cousin's wedding? That was a big deal since this was the first time that she traveled alone since she had the stroke. I felt nervous about it as soon as she walked into the security line and wished that I was going with her. Well, she had a great trip and a really good time. But, after being away from her exercise and diet routine, she came back and stepped back a little. I think she had some exhaustion from the travel. I know she will get back to it in time.

"Well, that happened to me. A friend of mine sent me some bran muffins from California. So, I just ate one and I had frozen them. Today, I ate four of them. Ha, ha, ha, ha…."

(Laughs) What! Four! Are they that good?

"Well, they are good, but I don't usually eat four at once."

Is it sugar?

"They're made with molasses. They're good. A friend of mine made them. But I don't do stuff like that. I ate four at one time. I used to do things like that a long time ago. I understand what you say about eating right.

This is the time that we should be eating tomatoes. The tomatoes are very good now. When I eat that good food, I feel better. My mind is better. Everything is better and that is why I've been feeling good. But in regard to what is going on with your mother, I ate four muffins."

I can't even see that!

"Like the four muffins, your mother got off track when she went to Vegas. I understand that. It will probably take a while for her to get back up to herself."

Did you notice any effect on your playing Sonny? When you are on a clean diet, does that affect your playing?

"I would say that it had a cumulative effect over the years. I had gotten to the point where I ate pretty well. I don't eat red meat. I don't eat sugar. This has been my way for many years. I eat very little salt and don't add salt. I have been on this clean diet and it definitely has helped my creative mind and my general mind functioning."

I simply feel better when I am eating well. Feeling better makes everything better.

"Exactly. And I know the difference. I know what it is to feel logy and full of junk food. It makes a difference in general. I know it can take a long time for people to get the message that exercise and clean foods make them feel better. You have to keep working on them. It takes time for some people to get the message, but they are hearing you on some level. Eventually it will sink in. You have to keep encouraging them. I know from my own experience."

What experience are you referring to?

"When I was messed up a long time ago, on drugs, people were telling me, and I knew I should stop but I never did. Finally, it came to me that I had to do it. While I was being told and not doing it, it was getting into my brain. 'Hey man, you got to stop.' And one day I was able to get up the proper thought patterns and the proper right action and I was able to do it. But it took a while."

What finally made you do it? Were you sick?

"In a way, what made me do it, was my mentor, my jazz idol, Charlie Parker. I was playing with Charlie Parker. He was addicted, and he knew that some of his band, his proteges were following him. It destroyed his life. He was very distraught by the fact that all these young kids were following his drug life.

I was on a record date with him and I told him that I had been clean and that I was okay. He was so happy to know this. Later somebody at the session ratted on me and told him, 'Oh no Sonny was out with us last night getting high.'

When I saw the way he looked with disappointment, I realized that I was killing my idol. I also always had my mother with me. I was frequently a bad boy she had to correct. I did it for my mother and for Charlie Parker.

At that time, I was a pariah. People would see me coming down the street and they would cross the street. I was a bad boy."

I can't imagine that.

"I know. That was a long time ago. Life is a struggle. We have to struggle. That is why we are here, to fight the good fight. We are here to learn. Why else would we be here? To have a good time? No. We are here to fight and to try to get enlightenment. Learn something."

I am thinking about what you just said. I have a vision of Charlie Parker in my head because my mother did a painting of him. So, I can see his face and I can imagine the way that you felt when he showed you his loving disappointment and how powerful that was for you.

"Yes. It was powerful and right then I said I've got to stop this stuff. Then I went away. It was a very important time in my life, but it showed that life is a struggle. You've got to fight for what is right."

He affected you immensely. He was an idol in your art and then also he challenged you to go beyond where he was by his loving desire for you to do better than he had done. That is beautiful.

You know that you have that capability in many ways for other people.

"I try to be a good model for kids and musicians. I get my fan letters. I got a really nice letter the other day. A saxophone player said that my music and my life had been a model for him. He had realized that there was more than just indulgence. More than just eating, sleeping, and buying things. He had followed me and done many of the things that I had done. He had learned that I have realized that there is more to life than just sensory enjoyment. Everybody really knows that, …but it is hard to do the things that make you grow and learn. Deep inside, we all know it. But, sometimes it can be hard to work through our karma and realize this truth. I am trying to do my part."

Do you answer the letters?

"Not often. There are too many of them. The point is that I got them, and they know that I got them. They felt they had to let me know what they felt, and I got it. They know that I get their notes."

Chapter 8

# Nature

*"When I am playing my spirit is at play.*
*Or I should say, I am in my spirit.*
*That is how it happens."*

As a young adult, I grew to appreciate the healing value of time spent in nature. When I felt depleted, a morning or afternoon in the garden was rejuvenating. If the exhaustion was exceptionally strong, time spent absorbing the brilliant energy of our sun would reboot my spirits. As the results of stress mounted in my body and mind I knew I had to get out to the sun. Any small spot in my yard that allowed me to feel the rays would work.

Sitting there, initially, my awareness was on my weakened physical and/or emotional state. Then there was full surrender as I accepted and connected with the fact that I needed some help. I took deep breaths and opened my heart to the warmth of the rays that would comfort me. The benefits were immediate. After a soaking session, I was able to get on to my gardening. Pulling weeds made me feel that I had some control in my life, which I had perceived was overwhelming and possibly out of control. The ugly, angry, overbearing, vicious weeds were taking over my beloved innocent plants. They had to go and were pulled and discarded. There were people in my life who I perceived had similar roles in my life. I could not pluck them from my life, but I could remove these weeds. A section of the garden would become the object of my attack. I pulled and plucked them with strength, fervor and pleasure. After they were gone, and in the trash, I surveyed the section and felt great satisfaction and relief.

The other benefit of the gardening was that it gave my mind a pause. The time spent concentrating on getting rid of each one of the nasty weeds, took my focus off any present, past, or future concerns. It was convenient, free, easy and therapeutic.

In my Ayurvedic studies, I learned about prana, life energy. It is the energy that animates the physical being and transforms it from static immobile physical matter into life.

Being in nature enhances our connection to our prana. This is exactly the experience that I had with my sun and my garden.

Prana is enhanced by being in nature, near bodies of water, in the mountains, in the wilderness, and in any natural environment. It is enhanced by natural sounds or primordial sounds.

There is a large amount of scientific data that confirms the healing benefits of spending time in nature. Patients who are post-op and able to view natural scenes from their hospital beds have shorter postoperative hospital stays and take fewer pain killer doses when compared to similar patients who had a view of a wall from their hospital beds. Activities in the presence of nature lead to positive short-term and long-term health outcomes. The participation in outdoor activities is correlated with less depression.

Ayurveda teaches the benefits of eating a rainbow of foods or foods of all colors at every meal. Numerous studies have repeatedly shown the benefits of multicolored fruits, and vegetables that are full of vitamins, minerals, fiber and phytochemicals. In addition, to the chemical benefits, there is a benefit from stimulating your eyes by appealing colors that improve your appetite and stimulate digestion.

Sonny, how are you doing this Monday morning?

"Chris, it's all good. Whatever is happing in the universe, even if I don't understand it. That is because I am not wise enough to look at the big picture. It's been very cold, but things are getting ready to change here."

Do you have property that allows you to get outside?

"I've got property and I've got a pond that I could walk around."

You know it is good for you to get out in nature. Connecting with nature is healing and helps to connect you with your spirit. The sounds and the views of nature are very healing.

"That's true. I am working up to being able to get out and do that more."

Didn't you tell me that you have a patio or a deck? You can get the benefits of the view.

"I can get out there. There are a lot of trees around here, so I don't have an expansive view of the sky and the stars. But I have the pond and deer and bears."

Have you seen any of them?

"I have never seen them. But they come by and go through your garbage and strew it on the driveway. They are looking for food. They are harmless though. They don't bother with people. But they are wonderful. They are nature and they were here before we were."

Are you doing your exercise? If you can't get out, I want you to walk at least ten minutes in that long hall you have.

"I am working on that. I have been doing my breathing exercises, my pranayama. Being a performer who played a wind instrument, I do it all the time without even thinking about it. Breathing deeply helps. When I did palates, my instructor taught me to not only take deep breaths from the stomach but to take deep breaths from the sides and all around the stomach. When I did that I found that there was so much more breath that I could take in. There is much more to know about things like this. Natural things that help us to be healthy."

Prana is your breath or life force. You can breathe in life force or prana from every part of your body. You can breathe prana into your skin or into the top of your head. You can visualize your spiritual force above you and breath it into every part of your body. Breathe in not just air, breathe in life force.

"Yes, life force. I agree. I leave my window open and breathe in a lot of fresh air. We have had a very mild winter. Every day it goes down to 18 or 19. But for just a few days, it has gotten down to single digits. But then it gets up to 50. I think that the planet is changing with global warming. I have the heat on. But, I can have the window open so that I can breathe a lot of fresh air."

Are you able to see any beautiful nature from your window?

"Oh yes. I can see my pond. It is beautiful. Naturally beautiful."

Good. That is very good for you.

"Yes. Absolutely. I am doing everything that I can to be healthy. Just realize how beautiful our creation is. The creation, I should say. There is so much that is just beyond comprehension. There is much that people miss. There is much to be aware of all around us. And, it's all good."

I wanted to tell you that I saw a video posted on your website of you playing at the Paris Jazz Festival in 1965. It was you, Gilbert Ravine and Arthur Taylor in black and white. It was amazing.

"Yes. I heard that was going up. I remember that. I think I was wearing a beret."

Yes, you were. I was not looking at the beret though I was amazed at how you handled your sax. Do you know what I was looking at?

"What?"

I was looking at how you handled that horn. I noticed that when I first saw you perform. You handle the sax like it is the weight of a feather. It could have been more like a pipe.

"That's my third arm. Everybody says that's my third arm. It all becomes part of me when I play. It happens naturally."

That is exactly what it looks like. As if there is no separation between the sax and you. It moves so much with you it looked like it was encompassed in your physical being.

"I 've heard that. More than this, when I am playing my spirit is at play. Or I should say, I am in my spirit. That is how it happens."

It was quite a video. I am glad that it was posted. There were many appreciative comments made about it. Many people were very happy to see it and they made very nice comments about you. Do you ever read those comments? They are so fun.

"No. I don't care about that kind of thing. I'm glad that it reaches people in a positive way. That is good. Then I've done my job. That's enough. I don't need to look at it and marvel over it and think, oh gee, look how good I am playing. Then it becomes a different thing. That is not my thing."

I also saw something recently about the documentary that you participated in about John Coltrane. Have you heard anything about it?

"It was done quite a while ago. They tell me that it went well, and they liked it. But I have not seen it at all. It was good talking about Coltrane."

You told me that they talked about the presumed rivalry between you two.

"People create rivalries. That is sort of normal. But we both loved the music first and we loved each other as people and musicians. We were very close. The rivalry thing was okay for people who needed that kind of dynamic to exist in this world. For some people everything is about competition and rivalry."

How did you two get to be friends? With you both playing the sax, were you ever in a band together?

"Yes, we were in a band together. The first time that I played with John was with Miles Davis. Miles had a band and we both played with him in the band."

That must have been quite a band.

"Yes. That was great. I would guess this was about 1948."

You were both kids.

"I guess so. I am looking forward to the documentary. Anything that praises somebody like Coltrane is good. He was a guy who didn't care about things of this world. He was in this world, but he wasn't of this world. That will heighten the spiritual understanding of who he was."

So, you were in a band together before either one of you was very famous.

"Well, famous? At that time, nobody was famous. Miles Davis wasn't famous."

Do you have good memories of that time with all the energy between the three of you?

"Ha, ha, ha, ha…. Yes. We also had a great guy playing drums. A guy named Kenny Clark, who went to Europe to live. He was called Klook. He influenced a lot of people that followed him. Max Roach was one that followed him. He was a great drummer. He remained in France for all of his career. So, it was a great experience. The first time that I played with Coltrane and Miles with Kenny Clark on drums was fantastic."

Was any of that recorded?

"I don't think that any of that was recorded. But you never know. I am not sure. I think Miles Davis spoke about that night in his autobiography. Coltrane has done a lot of beautiful music. Miles has done a lot of beautiful music. I've done some beautiful music. Duke Ellington has done a lot of beautiful music. So, the energy of Jazz has sustained people. It always will. As long as the world is here that music will be here.

How are your studies coming along? Learning about Ayurveda?"

Yes. I am getting ready for my meditation certification. I am reading about Patanjali.

"Patanjali. That is my main man. I wrote a song about him. Patanjali was one that talked about things that most people would say is impossible."

I am learning about him. When I get done I want to talk to you about it.

"I will be glad to hear. You could probably tell me some things about him."

That would be nice for a change.

Chapter 9

# Patanjali

*"I am not the body. You are not the body*
*This is very important to understand.*
*The body is going to deteriorate.*
*We are not the body.*
*Even when our body dies on this planet,*
*We are not dying. We are alive.*
*Our soul never dies.*
*There is no such thing as death."*

The name Patanjali is well known to Sonny's fans because it is the name of one of his most popular songs. I was very familiar with this name for this exact reason. When I was studying for my certification to teach meditation, the book, *Yoga Sutras of Patanjali* was part of my curriculum and required reading.

As my conversations with Sonny continued, I became aware that many of his concepts were those that he learned early in his studies of texts of Vedanta. The colossal interpretation of this wisdom has fascinated and inspired me since our first conversation.

As my studies deepened and our conversations continued, Sonny described teachers and books that had inspired him. Many of these were the same sources that my personal path had independently led me to pursue. As this unfolded, I marveled at the universal plan for me. It was exactly the right time for me to gain more profound knowledge and understanding of this wisdom. This was confirmation and evidence that I was exactly where I was meant to be.

I learned that Patanjali was a sage who lived about 2000 years ago. He was an inspired teacher of Vedanta which is an ancient collection of wisdom. He taught that yoga is the settling of the mind into silence, and only when the mind is silent can we realize our true nature, the effortless being of the self.

He is well known for defining the eight limbs of yoga which are daily practices that bring one closer to unity with the true higher self. In the United States the fifth limb of yoga, or asanas, is the only yoga limb that is well known. Asanas are body movements that flow with the breath. These movements are taught in yoga studios all over the world. Few people know about the other limbs of yoga. There is a limb of yoga that describes breathing exercises. Another limb describes personal behavior like nonviolence, truthfulness, and integrity. There are descriptions of social behavior like honesty, simplicity, contentment, and purification. Meditation and the practice of withdrawal of the senses are also limbs of yoga. There are also yoga limbs of intention and of a settled mind or intellect.

Sonny had a clear understanding of all these principles or limbs of yoga. He studied in India. I was very surprised to learn this and enjoyed it when he shared some of this experience with me.

Sonny, how are you today?

"I am fighting the right fight. Everything is cool. You know it's all good. Whatever we encounter in life, we may not understand why, but it's all good. One day we will understand it."

Last time we talked you mentioned to me something about doing yoga before yoga was popular in this country. I've been thinking about it ever since then, wondering how in the world did you find yoga?

"I read a book called, *The Autobiography of a Yogi*."

Very famous book. I know of it but have not read it.

"Yes. That book impressed me so much. I thought, wow. Of course, I had been interested in this kind of thought anyway. But *Autobiography of a Yogi* really turned me around. So, at that point, I decided that I wanted to investigate more. When I went to California some years later, I went to The Self Realization Fellowship, the place of Paramahansa Yogananda in Pacific Palisades. He had passed along. He transitioned not long before I went there. He made a wonderful contribution to this world we live in. Then I went to India to study yoga. I stayed there for over four months. I lived in an ashram. I had a wonderful time there. The swami that was there was knowledgeable. Some years later I invited him to speak in the United States. He spoke at Saint Peter's Church. This was sort of the musician's church. I maintained my ties to that ashram after he left."

When was this Sonny? Was it before you became "the Colossus"?

"Ha, ha, ha, ha…."

(Laughs). Or after?

"I was given the name 'Colossus' after an album I did in 1957. So, this is after that. I came back from India in 1967. It was really a wonderful experience and I have been studying since. It is a lifetime understanding and a lifetime pursuit. I am still into it very much now. You know there are different kinds of yoga. There is much more than the kind when you see people on the floor twisting their bodies. That kind of yoga became very popular in the United States. People wanted a way to exercise. That's fine. That's okay. But that's just one type of yoga. That's called hatha yoga. But there are many other kinds of yoga. They all relate to helping a person to develop their spirituality."

You said that you were in the ashram for four months. Did you actually stay there? How does that work? When you decided to go there, what did you do? Did you just show up?

"I decided that I needed to go to India because I wanted to find out more about this discipline. I took my horn with me. Got one bag and traveled to India. At that period of time, there were a lot of European's going to India. Like the Beatles and other famous people. They were all discovering India. The Maharishi Mahesh Yogi was well known. A lot of people were looking for that wisdom.

When I was on the plane, I met an Indian fellow. We were talking, and he told me about this particular ashram. I ended up going to it. At this particular ashram there were European people there when I arrived. There was a European movie star, some other people from Europe and some Indian people as well. They were all seekers after truth and knowledge.

I stayed there not far from Bombay or what is called Mumbai now. I had a chance to take several trips into Bombay where there was an Indian musical group. I wanted to hear them and got to hear them.

There were Indian people in the area who were jazz fans. Somehow, they found out that I was in India. I don't know how they found out. There was an Indian guy who was a big fan and came out to the ashram. He was a well-to-do jeweler and he introduced himself. He just showed up and said, 'I heard that Sonny Rollins is here.' So, I met him. A few years later the guy had a couple of Indian festivals, at which I performed. I came back, and I performed and met people there. I met one of my very close friends who is living here now in Arlington, Virginia. Anyway, that is sort of a side story. The real story is that I got a lot out of my visit there."

When you say that you got a lot out of it, I want to hear about that.

"One of the important things, I always had trouble when I was in the States, sitting down and quieting my mind. Getting into a lotus position and meditating. It was hard for me to do that. Because I was in the city all of the time and always had noise going in the background just like I do now. I've got the radio on. You can probably hear it. I told my swami that I was having trouble with meditation because I could not quiet my mind. I was just not used to doing that. He said, 'Sonny, when you play your horn, you are meditating. You don't have to worry about sitting down in the lotus pose. You are meditating."

Then you were meditating a lot playing your horn.

"Well, yes. This is really true because when I play I don't want to think about anything. I want to leave it to the subconscious. You only think up to a point. To get you started, and then you don't want to think. People say, 'What do you think when you are playing?' And I say, I don't want to think. The last thing I want to do is think. Do you understand what I mean? I am letting it happen. I let the music come to me. I don't want to think to get the music. The music has to get me. So that was a very important thing that I learned from my travel. Besides spending time in India, which is a fascinating place. I know you have been told."

Yes, I am hearing and learning. But I am way late on this. I'm catching up and I look forward to going there.

"It's fantastic. Now it was much more I am sure that things have changed some since the 60's. When I travel back to places it appears that things have deteriorated some. But that being the case, it is a fascinating place."

Now that you are not playing, how are you meditating?

"Today I am a little more advanced then I was then. I am involved in other kinds of yoga 24-7. I am always meditating in a sense. I am growing in spiritual knowledge. This is the little world. I am interested in the big world. All of yoga is trying to get you the understanding of the bigger picture. It's a joining or unity of mind and spirit. So that you are not just a body. You are also not your mind. You are that higher being.

You learn to put this world in its proper place which is a very small place."

When you were in India, did you change your diet?

"Yes. The food at the ashram was traditional Indian food. It was good clean food. They were not serving hot dogs! It was certain kinds of food. They served sattvic food. This is food that is most pure and nourishing."

Did you still follow the diet after your trip?

"Oh yes. Especially now. I don't eat any red meat. I don't eat any sweets."

Except for the occasional detour with your gift of muffins.

"Ha, ha, ha, ha…. Right."

I have been reading the *Yoga Sutras of Patanjali*. When people see the name of your famous song, "Patanjali" do they ever ask you what is means? Who is Patanjali?

"On occasion, I have been asked that. You know that the books have students who give their interpretation of the aphorisms in the beginning of the book and then at the end you have the actual aphorisms."

Yes, I have seen that.

"In the beginning of the book these are scholars who talk about the aphorisms. It's good to read that also but the aphorisms from Patanjali are at the end of the book."

The explanations are good for me because they provide a lot of history and then the actual sutras are very simple and beautiful.

"Yes. To accomplish these things! What is important is what he said. All trying to get closer to the understanding of what is the purpose of life. He had the light. Patanjali! It's a beautiful life when you realize that it is not this physical life that you have to concentrate on. It's not that this life is not important. It's very important. But it's only important that it leads you to the inner higher life. We have to use this life to get to this higher life or we are wasting this lifetime. Then we will have to come back and reincarnate, over, and over again. After gaining a level of consciousness we are able to have discussions like this. You are able to engage in the work that you are doing. You weren't just randomly born and turned into a doctor. There is a reason that you are a doctor. It didn't start when you were born. It started before that."

This higher level of consciousness is the source of our intuition and desires. They guide us on our spiritual path. I know that is where all of our deepest desires come from. I decided to be a doctor when I was four. Far too young to know what that was all about.

"Well you decided before that. You decided to be a four-year old that wanted to be a doctor. Your previous spiritual experience led you to be Chris Theard, M.D., a doctor."

I came across the picture of you, Dad and me in your dressing room at Jaun-les-Pins after your show. I thought about how long ago that was and how things led to this moment right now.

"Well it is really not so many years later. If you look at life as a huge picture that is always evolving, but you can recall things and feel like they happened only yesterday. The time dimension is not understandable to most people. I am going to tell you one more thing that is very important in Eastern thought. I am not the body. I am not the body. I am not the body. You are not the body. This is very important to understand. The body is going to deteriorate. We are not the body. Even when our body dies on this planet, we are not dying. We are alive. Our soul never dies. There is no such thing as death. You have to remind yourself of that. You are the spirit beyond the body. The body dies. You will never die. The soul is eternal. Have you got that?"

I got it Sonny. A spirit having a human experience.

"You got it."

# Chapter 10

# Meditation

*"Because wherever I go, I'm there.*
*So, I have to make sure that*
*I am comfortable within myself.*
*Enlightened, so that I can be anywhere,*
*and it doesn't matter where I am."*

While exploring Sonny's spiritual journey, I was enjoying my personal evolution and noticing benefits. My meditation was consistent, and I had observed many positive changes. Changes in my blood pressure happened rapidly. Other things changed more gradually.

I found that the time spent in meditation in the morning was like gold for the rest of the day. I could clearly identify a difference in the tone and the feel of the day. While the business of my packed schedule was a constant, my perception of the stress of the day was far less on the days that I meditated.

When I chose to stay in a solo practice I chose to do many of the jobs in the office that typically belong to nurses and technicians. Initially I could not afford to pay other staff and did all these jobs to pay my overhead. Eventually, I grew to appreciate the experience of spending more time with my patients. While doing so, I am performing the work of the doctor, the nurse and the technicians. This requires constant high efficiency multitasking.

With meditation, I have noted that the day that used to feel like a continuous jumping from one thing to another became a day that flowed from one thing to another with seamless ease. Another benefit has been an increase in my energy level and productivity. There has also been an improvement in my ability to connect with my patients.

Studies have been showing the benefit of meditation for many years. There is scientific evidence that a meditation practice decreases stress, anxiety, depression, pain, and insomnia. There have been studies that show a decrease in cholesterol, and the incidence of heart attacks and strokes.

There is also an increase in attention, quality of life and in the general perception of happiness.

Harvard studies published in 2011 have confirmed that there are changes in the brain that happen with meditation. When the brains of people that meditate were compared to age matched controls, the meditators did not have the shrinking of cortical matter that is typically seen with age. They had increased cortical activity in areas of the brain that are associated with working memory and decision making. The brains of the 50-year-old meditators looked like brains of 25-year-olds.

There were significant changes seen in the brains of people who had done a daily meditation practice for only two months. There was an increase in the size or cortical thickening of the hippocampus which is the area of the brain associated with learning, memory and emotional regulation. There was also an increase in the size of the temporoparietal junction which is an area associated with perspective taking, empathy and compassion.

A decrease was noted in the size of the amygdala which is in the primitive brainstem. This is the site of our stress reaction, and a decrease in its size was associated with a decrease in the stress reaction.

All of the changes noted were correlated with the patients reports of changes in their experiences. Sonny discussed his experiences in regard to meditation with me.

"Chris how are your classes going?"

They are great. Today is the last day of my certification. I'm finished. I've had a great time here. I am lucky that the Chopra Center is close to my home. There are people here at the teacher training who have traveled from all over the world.

"Well Chris, your life is as planned. If you want to call it fortunate, you can. But you are here for a purpose. And things are going to happen to facilitate your purpose."

I'm feeling very fortunate and very inspired. It's easy to be inspired in this beautiful environment. I know you've been in some gorgeous places. What is your favorite place to be?

"Ha, ha, ha, ha…. You really want me to answer that question?"

Yes. If you could just be in any place in the world, where would you be?

"Now you see Chris, the thing is this. Wherever I am, I want to be content to be there. Having been in some places that you may be surprised about. For instance, there was a time in my life when I was sleeping in cars. This was in Chicago back in the 40's. Sleeping in places that were selling cars. They had some cars that were open, and we could get into them. Not break into them, just get into them"

Really. Tell me more about that.

"We were sleeping in cars to avoid the Chicago weather. You say, 'Wow.' But it was something that I went through and it was okay. I slept.

My main point is this. Having experienced all of this, it really doesn't matter to me where I am sleeping. I have been all over the world, but that is not important to me. I am not going to say that I would be able to survive now out in the cold. But that's okay. I think that I have survived enough in this life. So that is not on my radar at all.

I know a woman from South Africa who told me that I should be in Capetown because it is such a beautiful place. The weather is beautiful, and it has beautiful hills and the ocean. It does not matter where I am physically. It's where I am mentally.

There is no place physically that I am interested in. I have a home, but I am not interested in physical conveniences or in what a nice place it is.

You know at this point in my life, that is how I feel. I don't care about these outer things in the world anymore. I am not saying that there are not beautiful places that I haven't seen. Sure, of course there are but that's just not my desire. Because wherever I go, I'm there. So, I have to make sure that I am comfortable within myself.

Enlightened, so that I can be anywhere, and it doesn't matter where I am. I don't concentrate on being in a beautiful place by the ocean or by the beautiful mountains. It would be good. But, it's not enough. I've been in some beautiful places and I've been in some places that you would consider not beautiful. Like I just told you about. But it's still about me being there.

I have to make sure that I, my spirit, my soul has got to be in a certain place, a certain level of understanding of what the whole thing is about. Do you understand what I am trying to say?"

Yes.

"You have to have understanding that it is not about the physical. It doesn't matter where your body is. It's about where your spirit is. I was talking about Chicago recently to a friend of mine. We were in Chicago back in the 40's. We were talking about it and I recounted that situation about sleeping in parked cars."

Wow.

"Ha, ha, ha, ha….".

I did not expect to hear you say anything like that. Tell me more. Were you performing then?

"I was old enough, but I was sort of into a drug situation. That is what was controlling my life at that time. Sure, I was playing but I wasn't able to do much playing under those circumstances.

We did play at that time, but I was carrying the stick. Do you know what that means?"

No. What does that mean?

"Ha, ha, ha, ha…. this is funny. Back in the 30's during the depression, when things were a little rough, there were people that they called hobos. Have you heard of hobos?"

Yes.

"Hobos had no home, so they would have a stick and, their belongings were tied to a stick."

Oh. I've seen pictures of hobos with sticks.

"Ha, ha, ha, ha…. So that is where the expression of carrying the stick comes from. So that's why I used that expression. But sure, I was playing. In the forties I was playing, and I met a lot of great musicians in Chicago. Because of my innate talent I got to play a lot of places. But I was just as a raggedy guy carrying a stick."

(Laughs). Raggedy guy! I can't see that!

"Ha, ha, ha, ha…."

Tell me this. I am wondering how the drugs affected your creativity?

"Well, you must remember this.

That's a song, "You Must Remember This." But, you know, many artists of every stripe, whether they were writers, whether they were musicians, or painters, people who use art and try to express things and divine qualities of life, they often use some kind of substance. whether it's opium, alcohol, cocaine, they use something that gets them out of the humdrum of everyday life. And that's why you find many artists all through history, indulging in something. Because they are trying to get their mind out of their daily lives. They are trying to get their mind out of the ordinary into the extraordinary. Even Yohan Sabastian Bach used to play for beer. He would do a concert and be paid in beer."

Do you think it is used to escape their present issues and mind to connect more with their creativity?

"I don't discount that because I am sure that it can happen. However, in our world, this world, we have to live a certain way. By doing this we are escaping our karma and it is not productive."

I just heard that concept this week in class. You must work through karma to get beyond it. If you try to escape it, or if you create more negative energy by reacting to the situation negatively, you make it worse and you create more bad karma by your negative reaction.

"Exactly."

Do you think that your meditation has replaced drugs to connect you to your higher levels of creativity and performance?

"Meditation is definitely a tool for me. Remember that my Guru told me, 'When you play your horn, that is meditation.' So that I was able to go through my life playing my horn and seeking meditation in that way.

I have always told people that my technique is not having technique. I don't want to think about it. I want to go to another place where my physical mind is not active. I am getting a flow through my mind from a higher level. Let the music play itself. That is the level that you want to get to in meditation. Meditation can be done in a lot of ways. It has a very good role in helping to calm the mind and connect to the other higher place. This is much better than using other harmful substances. After I stopped the drugs, I got to that high place with my horn. This was much better. A much higher level. People get to that high level of awareness with meditation."

Our true self, our higher self is manifested in and living in our bodies. We have to take care of our body. You should not poison it with toxins if you plan to live in it.

"You know this is a difficult thing. Being a drug addict at one time in my life, I know how hard it is to give up these addictions. It was really difficult for me and I know that it is difficult for people to do it. It gives them some kind of drink of water in the dessert of life. This is where the problem comes in. If a person can realize it for themselves that is the only way that this can happen."

Well the fear of death of your body should be compelling. While we know we have a greater place in our existence with our soul. If we value anything that is in this manifestation and we want it to continue in a healthy high-quality way, we must take care of our physical health.

"This is such a question about life and death. It is hard to tell people what to do and what not to do. It is in the human condition to be afraid to die and afraid of the unknown. On the other hand, I don't think it is good to be afraid of anything. When you get to the critical stage of life it is hard for anybody to tell anyone else anything. They have to figure it out for themselves."

In the beginning of our meditation we ask soul questions. The first question is, "Who am I?" This is a question to connect us with our higher self rather than the roles we play. The second question is, "What do I want?" The third question is, "What is my purpose, or dharma?" And every time I ask that question I'm waiting to see the answer. Sometimes it's something bigger or more than I expected. Whatever it is I stay open and I keep moving down the path toward the next step.

"And you don't know what it may be. What you are doing now is an inspiration. Who knows what you will be doing eventually. That is a hard one to think about. What does this lead to? I don't know what it leads to, but I know that the path is right. I don't think about what it leads to. That's up to the higher power. So that last question would stifle me. It's hard to know that."

Yes. But just being open to whatever it is and feeling that you are going with the flow. That last question is, "What am I grateful for?"

"That is a beautiful question. There is always a lot to be grateful for. That is a very good question."

There is so much to be grateful for. .
gratitude the energy elevates. It cha
frequency.

I am grateful to be able to take care o
bring this natural healing to them.

"You have been chosen to teach them. This is very
heartening and encouraging that you are able to do this. I can
see it all clearly. It is part of this beautiful place that we are
in. What is going on there around you. It's all good."

# Chapter 11

# Knowing

*"It's not day by day,*
*it's more like forever by forever.*
*We are involved in something that is*
*much more than day by day.*
*The universe is about love."*

When I was four years old my brothers and I were on the floor in front of my parent's bed watching one of the first situation dramas. The show was set in a medical practice and a male physician and female nurse were on the screen. I watched the show and noted their interaction.

I looked up at my Dad and said, "Daddy, when I grow up I want to be a nurse."

He enthusiastically responded, "Nursing is a wonderful profession. You would make a wonderful nurse. You can do anything that you want to do."

I went on watching the show and then a few minutes later, I turned around and said, "Daddy, when I grow up I want to be a doctor."

My father smiled and responded, "That is a wonderful profession. You would be a wonderful doctor. You can do anything that you want to do."

I held a strong desire to be a doctor from age four and started preparing for medical school when I was in high school. I took Latin and every science and math course that was available.

When I was in my first semester of medical school, my grandmother died after her third heart attack. I was horrified that this could happen to my precious grandmother. This drew me to cardiology because I wanted to learn all that I could to be sure that this did not happen to anyone else that I loved. But in medical school, I was advised by many that choosing cardiology would be a mistake. They advised that I should choose carefully. If I wanted to be a practicing physician and also have a family, they recommended fields like radiology, pathology and dermatology.

I wanted a practice and lots of kids. But, I was not inspired by these fields. I chose to do training in internal medicine. My desire to be an expert in cardiology persisted.

As I trained in internal medicine, my inspiration grew as I observed the importance of cardiology work. When I was in the ICU taking care of a critically ill patient with acute cardiac problems, I was immediately relieved when the cardiologist stepped through the ICU doors. I wanted to be that person, to be able to help my patients without calling for assistance. I decided to continue my training in cardiology.

When I was in my cardiology fellowship, I wanted to do interventional cardiology. This involves the practice of putting balloons and stents in coronary arteries to open up blockages. These procedures are critical and often done urgently while the patient is in the process of a heart attack. Since heart attacks frequently happen at night, the hours of an interventional cardiologist are unpredictable and can be very long.

There was only one female on the teaching staff during my cardiology fellowship. She told me that if I chose to do interventional cardiology, I would ruin my life.

She was referring to the demanding schedule in reference to her own personal desires. This did not apply directly to me. I was inspired by the practice. In the training process I found that I was fortunately very capable and blessed with required skillset to be an excellent interventional cardiologist. The procedures were challenging, critical, lifesaving and extremely fulfilling. The decision to proceed felt natural and it is clear that I made the right decision for myself when I chose to do interventional cardiology.

In the first years of my cardiology practice, I worked with a large group. After moving to California, I joined another group. After one year, I wanted to start a solo practice. I was told that it was impossible to make it as a sole practitioner in the area. By this time, I was not only an expert in cardiology, I was an expert at following my deepest desires and started my solo practice.

These inner callings guided me well. I had a successful busy practice and I had children. My first daughter was born when I was at the end of medical school and my first son was born after my first year of cardiology practice. My life with full time cardiology practice and two children was very busy. But, surprisingly, later I had a deep longing to have more kids. This seems to be very unreasonable, but this desire persisted and grew as my kids grew. I was told by many that I was too old to have more children.

However, this desire did not resolve. It turned into a longing. I dreamt about having more children and I knew that they must have been on their way. In 2006 I had triplets.

The driving forces that urged me to do all of these things were my deepest desires. These were inner whispers, and at time shouts from my spirit guiding me to the path that was in the direction of my personal journey. We all come to our lives with a set of desires or predispositions that guide us and direct us on our paths. They shape our decisions through our lives.

Sonny has always been guided by his deepest desires. He was drawn to the saxophone at a very young age and knew that he would be successful. He continues to be guided by his spirit to do what he was sent to this earth to do.

"Hello Chris, how is everyone?"

Everyone is doing well. Better every day.

"Oh definitely, because it's all good. The whole thing is good. We have to try to get that understanding. It's not day by day, it's more like forever by forever. We are involved in something that is much more than day by day. The universe is about love."

If everyone knew that, the world would be a better place.

"Well the world is a training ground for people to come through and find out how to live. If they don't do it this time they will have a chance next time. As the saying goes, pay me now or pay me later. Ha, ha, ha, ha, …. We are here to do things for others. To help others. When you figure that out you can feel it. When one is born with that wisdom, one is blessed."

I think it is easier when you figure that out.

"It's easier for you. How is everyone? Lowell? Your father Les?"

Recently Lowell was sick, but he is doing much better now. I was on the phone with him when you called the other day. I tried to flip over but you were already gone. When I went back to Lowell he sounded immediately better. As soon as he heard that I was talking to you, his tone changed.

"That's good. That is the other part of health. Nobody can measure the mental part of it. When you think better you feel better. If you talk to him tell him that he is in my thoughts."

Well I am going to have both my Dad and Lowell in my house on the 23rd. I am having a family gathering to celebrate my Mother's painting. She started painting again after her stroke and has done twelve family portraits in the past eight months. It is quite a miracle.

"This is great."

I am also celebrating my son's return home.

"I remember all about him. This is great news. He is back in the saddle again?"

He is so good. It's another miracle. He picked up right back where he left off. He is my same sweet boy that he always was before he left. He's kind, creative and loving. It's like there was a hurdle. He jumped right over it and picked up his normal life. He just started music production school. He is inspired and excited to get to school. I take that as a true sign that he is healed.

"Well I am glad that he appreciates that he is in a good position. Because life is short. We don't have a lot of time to get our act together. He has a great opportunity to get right into it. He is very fortunate to be back on his right track and to be able to follow his desires."

There is nothing in his way. He is naturally talented and very highly motivated. I am looking forward to his success. He is too.

Sonny you have told me that you had a knowing or understanding of not being just your body from a young age. What experience did you have as a young person that brought you that kind of wisdom?

"When I was a little boy, a youngster, I knew that there was a consciousness within me. A feeling that there was something besides me. I knew what to do and what not to do. Whether I followed it or not was a different story, but I always knew that presence was always in me."

But there were times when you did not follow your spiritual plan or flow.

"Oh definitely. I did all kinds of things that I am not proud of but that is not relevant because I have lived long enough to know what I did wrong and what I did right. It has been a journey. But I always had that feeling as a youngster regardless of what I did. It was always there.

When I was seven years old and got my first alto saxophone. I knew that I would be a prominent musician."

Did you really?

"Yes. Oh yes. I saw the whole thing."

How did you feel about the whole thing? Did that scare you as a child?

"Oh no. That excited me because I wanted to play the saxophone. This showed me what was going to happen. I was not only going to have my love playing my horn, I was going to be successful at it and be prominent."

That is a wonderful thing to see as a child. It's also wonderful to be open to the whole concept at that young age.

"I had a consciousness from early on and it was great. I know I got it on my spiritual journey having lived many lives."

Do you think that all of the things that happened to you along the way were a part of your spiritual journey?

"I guess it all did because it happened. I'm smart enough to know that there is a reason why my life was what it was and is what it is. I assume that anything that happened in my life happened for a reason. At times it was a rough life and that is what I had to go through and I am going through now. As a child I knew that I had a spiritual consciousness. But that did not mean that since I knew that from a young age that I would have a perfect life. Not at all."

When things did go wrong, do you think that this premonition gave you some reassurance that everything would be okay?

"No. Deep down of course but not on the surface. I was a youth like everybody else and did stupid things. Eventually it worked into my understanding a little bit more and it carried me through life. But at the time things just happened."

But when you fell off your path you managed to get back on it. You never decided to give up the horn.

"There was never a question about that. I can't go against the universe, no. It was my destiny. But as people go through life it is hard. The reason why I am who I am is because I have lived many lives to be who I am today. I am still getting through this life. I will get through this life and believe that I will have more enlightenment and I will be further along on the path."

Sonny, how do you feel about your success? How do you feel when you think about these things? And I am not talking about what everybody else thinks because we all know about that.

"Ha, ha, ha, ha, .... Well success I feel is never enough. I can only go by how I feel toward myself. I never have completed my earthly success. Since I have this pulmonary thing, I am not doing my music like I was heading for. That part is fine. It did not happen how I was working for.

But that is not negative. What happened, happened for a reason. As far as my success goes. It's not enough. I have to have more success because I am a human being that is trying to be perfect. I am still striving. I am still alive on this planet.

I never concentrate on my success, Chris. Because my success is yet to come. I am glad that I am able to have a good influence on other people. I have done three interviews this week. Doing these I have to recount my life. But I am interested in things of a spiritual nature."

Have you always felt this way about success being an ongoing experience?

"Pretty soon I got that revelation. I used to be stupid and had a big head. I thought I was great and all this stuff."

Oh, you mean like the rest of the world thinks. (Laughs)

"Ha, ha, ha, ha, ......"

I have a question for you. Did you ever get nervous when you were going to perform?

"Not really. If I look back, I was never nervous. There were always things that I was concerned about but not nerves."

Well you were clearly doing what you were meant to do. I remember seeing you in Perugia in front of 5000 people.

"No. No. I am worrying about things like, do I have a good reed on my horn, or, did we rehearse everything with the band. These are the things that I worried about."

But we are all performing in some way. You are performing, and you are on stage in your whole life. When people come to you to get help, you are in the role of a healer. This is just one of many roles that you play.

You were not born and then became a healer. You were born with that potential in your consciousness, in your spirit. You didn't just get the thought from nothing. You came into this life with this desire already. All of the necessary attributes were there at the time of your birth."

Yes, Sonny just like you came out of your mother's womb with a saxophone as a third arm. Right?

"Ha, ha, ha, ha, ...."

# Chapter 12

## You Have it All

### *"Won't nobody get me negative.*
### *No way!"*

The primitive stress response originates from the brainstem in an area which is called the amygdala. The natural design of this response was intended to activate changes in the body to prepare the being for responding to a serious life-threatening situation by either fighting or fleeing. Changes occur to increase the ability for the blood to clot if there is injury. There is increased heart rate and blood pressure and blood flow to major muscle groups to increase in preparation for a battle or intense physical exertion.

Hormonal changes occur to increase the availability of blood sugar as an energy source.

While these changes would be beneficial if we were facing a wild animal or any circumstance in which we have to fight for our lives, these changes are very harmful in other circumstances.

This primitive response is activated in moments that we may perceive as inconveniences or low levels of stress. Common examples are paying bills, waiting in traffic, relationship stress, and common kid stress. Others are work stress, the stress of multitasking activities or performance pressure. Being accustomed to multitasking or being highly skilled at multitasking and the ability to perform well under pressure do not remove the harmful physiologic effects of the stress response.

There are instantaneous bad effects from the activation of the fight or flight response and long-term negative effects. These changes increase heart attacks, strokes, infections, cancer, diabetes, asthma, obesity, dementia, gastric reflux disease, irritable bowel disease and premature death.

The week after the last Presidential election was a very difficult time for many of my patients. They came in to see me with strong stress reactions.

Hey Sonny, what's happening with you?

"I am fighting the fight. Fighting the good fight. Trying to fight the right fight, the good fight."

Oh good. Please don't fight a bad fight, only fight the good fight.

"That is right. We don't want to fight anyway. We want to survive. But everything is beautiful. The good fight is a good fight. So, how are you doing today?"

I'm okay. But, I'm having a difficult time at work because people are very upset.

"I know."

My patients bring this fear and stress in with them searching for my help. A lot of people are in crisis mode right now. So, it has been a stressful week.

"I know. It makes us dig deep. We have to find a way to deal with whatever happens in this life and find a way to make it right."

Sometimes it's necessary to remove yourself from issues. When you are watching and listening to the turmoil, it is easy to get pulled in. You've got to turn it off and step away. I've been advising people to turn off the news. But it is hard to do that. Especially, since there seems to be no time to recover from the last concerning issue, when the new concerning event is happening in real time.

"People have to dig deep inside of themselves and find out what they are about. Are they doing the correct thing in their lives? Be aware of everything that is right in their life.

And if we are trying our best, then we are covered. There is nothing that can happen on this planet that can supersede anything that is of a spiritual nature. The spiritual realm is the top of the mountain. So, we have to live there and sometimes, remove ourselves from what is happening around us. Things will always happen in this world.

Things feel worse now for a lot of people. They are realizing that some things are very bad. But this is not new. Look at the experience of black people in this country for all these years. In a way it's good to expose these feelings so that we can really know where we are.

This is a battle that many ethnic people have fought every day of their lives in this country. Now the rest of America appears to be more aware of this fight."

When I think about these issues I have flashbacks to the stories that I heard from my mother about her experiences of racism through her life. As Creole mixed-race kids, we experienced a lot when we moved from San Diego to Houston. We were ages five to thirteen and we were terribly bullied by the kids in our all white neighborhood.

"Well that is this world. That is how things are down here on this planet. That is behavior that is not connected to the universal spirit, God or energy."

I know. It is ridiculous since human beings share the same DNA. We are essentially the same physically. The genes that make us look differently are a small fraction of our

DNA. The outside coverings are different, but the inter organs and complex physiology are the same for all human beings.

"Don't be surprised by this going on. This is how it is."

You are right we have been reminded that this is how it is. And then people who look the same want to hate each other because they have different religions. There will always be something that a person can find to dislike about someone else if they chose to be negative, judgmental or intolerant. It is a struggle.

"Exactly. But it is a winnable struggle. Because you do not let this type of negative thinking get you down. You cannot do that. You have to live your life. You have to be a good person. Be sure that you are being the kind of person that you want to be. Are you being kind and generous? That is what you have to do. Then it doesn't matter what else is going on out here."

You are right. I am consistently doing my best. That's all that I've got.

"Well that is all you have, and you have it all. Rather than saying that is all you have, I would say you have it all.

Nobody on this planet can change that. In this world it is small stuff. All of this fear and people worrying about dying. You have to realize that there is no such thing as death. We change but we don't die. So, so what.

friend that I worked with at my record
ɔ her about this kind of thing and she used
y, what if the Ku Klux Klan comes by and
ɔ, I told her, look, if the Ku Klux Klan shoots
mɩ,              ɛir problem. It is not my problem.

I am ɩot supposed to live in this life forever. Nobody lives in this life forever. Buddha and Jesus didn't live here on earth forever. So what. As long as I am doing the right thing, being kind to other people, not trying to mess over other people, treating others as I want to be treated, then I am fulfilling what I am meant to do spiritually. And that is all that it is about. My body is going to turn to dust like everything else on the planet. I am not my body. Times like these are times that we have to realize that. It's all about where you are spiritually. We have to dig deep and pull that up."

There is a wonderful word that you have mentioned to me before that has become one of my favorite words. It is "equanimity," an evenness or calmness no matter what the situation. I take it further to mean happiness no matter what the situation. I am working on being in the moment and finding equanimity no matter what.

All we have is right now in our human experience. When we get bogged down on fear we are stuck in that reality which does not actually exist right now. We can have bad memories of the past or a fear of the future that highjacks the present moment. If we let that happen, we are not living, and we lose all of these moments. There is no value in that.

"Of course! It's a waste of time."

Not only is there no positive value, it makes people sick. I've seen it all week.

"Absolutely. Now they have to understand how to deal with that. You deal with that by being a better person yourself. You be as good as you can be. And realize that this world is the little picture. Not the big picture. People ask me about where we go after we leave here. I don't know. That is not my business.

All my business is to do right while I am here. That is my business. Don't worry about what happens. Think about eternal things. Not stuff that's happening every day. We have to try to get it all together while we are here. So that we will be ready for the next level. When you are thinking positively, and you are doing what you have to do you are on the right track.

Do your best to try to calm these people down. They have to be concerned with making themselves better. It's not just about making money and enjoying yourself. And, of course, anything that involves hurting someone else is not good."

I'm trying to shift their energy from fear. I've been trying to get my patients to focus on gratitude. There is always something simple to be grateful for…health, clean water, air, a beating heart, safety. When they shift their focus to this moment and to a place of gratitude their energy immediately changes. This has been a good tool to pull them to the present moment and to stop fear.

"Yes. But there are a lot of people who are not physically safe. You have to be safe inside of yourself. Look at people who have war all around them. People are always fighting and killing people. It is the reality of this world. Rather than searching for safety in the outside, you have to feel safe inside and know that you are not of this world no matter what is going on around you."

Connecting to the higher power that is your true higher self? The self that has no beginning and no end?

"Yes. Now you are talking. That is who you really are. So, you can be safe no matter where you are because you know that you are far more than the body. You are far greater than this physical being.

All fear comes from feeling that you are not connected to the true self. Yes, we live in our body. It is hard for people to get that concept. A lot of people think that they are their bodies and that is all there is. I don't critique anybody. We all can think what we want. That's fine. I am trying to get myself together. I am not going to tell anybody they are wrong. I let them live how they want to live. But, I am working on myself. I am not going to do anything that is wrong. I will not hurt anybody. I will do unto others as I would have them do unto me. When you realize that there is much more than this world then you can deal with this world. Other than that, this world is crazy. People with guns trying to hurt people. If I had to defend myself, I would defend myself. But that has nothing to do with the universal God. The universal truth and God. The truth as taught by many, Buddha, Patanjali, many sears through the ages and Jesus Christ.

But the real Jesus Christ. Not the one they had painted in my church when I was a little boy growing up. That painting is a representation of man. I am talking about the real essence of the being. Doesn't have to be a guy with blue eyes and blonde hair."

When you were a child did your mother take you to church?

"Yes. I went to church and Sunday school. After that I grew away from the church. I always had a feeling inside of me that there was something bigger going on. I always knew that there was a voice or a presence that was bigger than anything."

What kind of church was it?

"It was Christian. My mother came from the Caribbean. We went to a Moravian church. Later, I went to other churches. The AME Zion church in New York when I was a little older, the Baptist, the next block from where I was born. My grandmother used to take me to the gospel churches all over Harlem. The storefront churches. The music was great. Them cats would be playing, blowing in there. Mother Horn and all those gospel people. I've been all around the church clock."

You haven't told me much about your mother. You said that she was from the Caribbean. Where?

"She was from Saint Thomas."

Oh. There is a song by that name. I've heard it. (Laugh's)

"Yes. And my grandfather was from Haiti. He was a doctor in Haiti. Doctor Solomon. I don't think about that part of the past now. I think about trying to live my life now in the proper way. I am grateful. Just like you said earlier. When you wake up and you've got your health and you can breathe, you've got your mind and you can think, that is something to be grateful for."

You said that your grandmother took you to many churches, what was she like?

"My grandmother was a very strong woman. She was an activist. She used to take me with her to civil rights marches up and down Lenox Avenue in New York for Marcus Garvey and Paul Robeson. We had an African flag in the house. When I was a little boy my grandmother would take me everywhere."

That was a wonderful experience to learn to stand up for yourself and for others.

"Yes. When I began playing music and got a little reputation, I made the Freedom Suite in 1958. It was the first protest songs. It was a trio with Max Roach and Oscar

Pettiford. My producer took a lot of heat for the record. I took some heat for it too. I was confronted about it. But it wasn't a big deal for me because it was normal for me to be marching against what was going on. I grew up with that. So, it was no problem for me to be aware.

I recorded the "Negro National Anthem" on *The House I Live In*. "The House I Live In" was a song that Paul Robeson sang. He was a big hero of mine. He was a real brilliant guy. He was a great athlete, Phi Beta Kappa in school. He was a great actor. He played Othello on Broadway and played in many black movies. He was an activist for his people and he was vilified for this. They barred him from performing. He had a short life. So that's how it goes."

Here we are right now still fighting some of these same fights.

"It's the same thing. It's no different. It's up to us to try to move it up as we gain some knowledge and try to get closer to that light. As the Buddhist refer to the light. In the meantime, we are here trying to survive and going through our karma. Don't worry about all of this going on around you. Don't let the negativity get to you. I know it is normal to think about it. But don't let it get you sad."

I am working on it. It's a tedious process because the bad information keeps coming in with my patients all day every day.

"You've got to help your patients. Bring them up by telling them the things that we've been talking about. A lot of people have been feeling depressed and down. But it's okay. Now we see it and we will deal with it. Don't worry about it. Just keep trying to help people like you are doing. It's all good. We just have to get the wisdom to see where it's at. Take a higher perspective. It makes all the difference in the world. Won't nobody get me negative, no way!"

I love that. Won't nobody get me negative, no way! I'm going to take that Sonny. Thank you.

# Chapter 13

# Transition

*"I don't care about the body,
or what happens to it.
It's just dust.
Once my spirit, soul leaves here,
I don't care what happens.
I don't worry about what happens when I die.
It's a waste of time."*

The thought of sleep brings positive connotations. It is a primary part of our lives and our health. There are many studies that link medical problems with lack of sleep and it's easy for all of us to appreciate the rejuvenating and refreshing value of a good night of sleep. I have always believed that my spirit soared during sleep. In my studies of Vedanta there is support of my concept. Our fundamental being is our spirit and when we sleep we have contact with this higher consciousness. The bird flies through the day and must at some point settle down and perch sometime for rest. We function daily in our minds and bodies but like a tethered bird, have to return to our source. When we sleep we settle down to the true essence of ourselves.

Deep sleep is associated with a lack of awareness of the environment and a vulnerability to the environment. We have no concept of what is happening around us. When we go to sleep we always plan on waking up and have no concern that we are entering this other state of being.

This is not like the concept of the final human sleep which brings a lot of fear to many people. My first experience with death was at the age of seven when my best friend died of complications of a brain aneurysm. My mother told me she had died. I remember being very sad to lose my friend and wondering where she had gone. I did not understand how she could have just disappeared from existence. It did not make sense to me.

There was no other personal experience with death until my sweet, elegant, beautiful grandmother died in my first months of medical school. She was a loyal Catholic and there was the traditional wake and funeral for her in New Orleans. When I stood in front of her casket at the wake, I stared at her and was amazed at how she looked like she was just sleeping. It was disturbing to me because I knew that she was not sleeping. When I touched her ice-cold hand, I knew that she had been long gone and that her essence was very far away from the body that was in that box. I wanted to hold on to my memory of her beautiful, loving, gentle, and generous nature. She was always joyous around us and when she was amused by us, she would give us her glorious, signature, silent laugh.

When my brother died suddenly at the age of 32, we saw his body in a small room at the funeral home before he was cremated. On this devastating occasion, I sensed that he had just been there, but at the same time, he was no longer present. He had just gone. I looked at him and thought about how strange it was to appear so close to life and yet no air was moving in and out of his lungs. His breath, his life force, his prana was gone from this shell. Still I could feel his presence and knew that his essence, his being, was still very near.

My brother transitioned from his solid human form to his fundamental true spiritual state. Through our lives we transition through many roles. While we are the same essence of being we look completely differently as a baby or a child, a teenager or young adult, or as a young parent or grandparent. There is a frequent daily transition between the multiple roles that we play, like doctor, mother, daughter, sister, partner, friend. The one constant in these completely different roles is the higher being that directs them.

Just as we navigate the roles that we play, and we transition between them, we will transition from this present manifestation back to our spirit, our true selves, when this earthly journey is complete.

"Chris, you know what I thought of today? I was listening to the radio and they were talking about some fighting happening in Iraq. I was thinking about how I would be if I was somebody living in that place with people bombing around me and complete chaos.

I realized that when you get, so called, killed, you immediately are beginning your next journey. So all of these people who are killed in this bombing and violence may be going on to a new opportunity. If you don't think like this, you would always be asking, how can the world be so cruel? How can people get killed, maimed and blown up? Sure! It is terrible. Just like the people who got swept away in the tsunami. You have to know that the minute that they got drowned, they went to another place. Could be a beautiful place. Nobody knows how it is. Why do we have to assume that it was a terrible alternative. We have no idea about this. In this world people have a narrow idea of the infinite world. People say, my friend died and it's so sad. But, no.....no! You don't die. You've gone on to another existence."

That is a concept that requires an understanding that you are not just the physical and mental contained in your body and that this is just one chapter, one manifestation.

"Many people think that this is the whole of everything. I probably thought that way at one time in my life. But I passed that kind of thinking a long time ago. I can't even think that way now. That was when I was in Kindergarten. Ha, ha, ha, ha…."

A long time ago. That is quite a concept. From a human perspective, these things appear to be so tragic. When in actuality, it may be a gift to the spirit to move on to another opportunity.

"Of course. That is what it is all about. I know that now."

Yes. But it is hard to grasp this concept while living in this human body and human mind with our human perspective and the limitations of our human understanding. But if you are connected to the concept that you are a higher self and that this is just a manifestation of body and mind then it should be harder to be attached to this human existence and physical manifestation.

"We must all get past that. I know that it may be a big concept for most people. There is devastation when we have loss of a loved one. You see them in the funeral home or in a casket."

Yes. I have found that to be very difficult. It's painful to think of a loved one in the ground. I found my grandmother's ceremony and the ritual around her body to be very painful. I wanted to remember her as she was when she was alive, not as that body dressed up in that box.

"It's horrible and painful."

I decided at that moment that I would never have any of that done for me. I will be cremated.

What do you think about that Sonny?

"Once my spirit, soul leaves here I don't care what happens. It doesn't matter. But, since we live on this planet and people think like this, of course I'm going to be cremated. It's much less expensive and much easier. The people who are still down here have to deal with it."

Well, I don't want whatever is left of me to be anywhere. I want my ashes scattered in the ocean or somewhere where they will disappear.

"I will tell you a funny story about that. I had a good friend who was an alto saxophonist. We taught together way back in Jim Crow and Jane Crow days. He passed on and got cremated.

His last wishes were as you said to be spread out over the ocean. So, some of his close friends went over the ocean in a plane. They found a good spot not far off of the shore. They opened the container and the wind was so high that the ashes blew right in their faces. So, he had the last laugh. Ha, ha, ha, ha...."

Oh my God! What did they do?

"What could they do?

So when you think about having your ashes spread out on the ocean, think of that."

That is horrible, and funny.

"He was probably laughing because he was that type of guy and he would know that would be a good joke. A parting joke."

Can you imagine going home covered in someone's ashes and then taking a shower and washing them down the drain?

"Well they are just ashes. It's so inconsequential. We are talking about the body. The body has many sheaths. The physical body is one sheath. After you leave that sheath you pass to another sheath.

Once I saw a friend of mine. He had passed away. I saw him in a physical form that was different from when he was alive. He looked something like how I had remembered him, enough that I knew it was him, but he was covered in another sheath."

Sheath, another layer or existence or covering.

"His soul was, who knows, maybe between this world and another. I don't need to know about this. The point is that when you see that body in a casket or anywhere else after death that body was just a covering. The soul has moved on and is somewhere else in another sheath."

Well think of all the coverings that we have in our earthly existence. We have a covering as a baby, a child, a teenager, young adult, older adult and then as a more elderly adult. Those coverings are all completely different. Different sizes, different looks, different perceptions, thought processes, different beliefs and different knowledge base. All of these are within our lifetime. These are all different coverings during this physical manifestation all from the same spirit.

"Yes. So when you are laying in a casket, you leave your body which is still existing in ether world. I know that right away there is a place where the soul exists that can be perceived here. Who knows for how long, but this is another sheath."

I understand what you are saying. When my brother died suddenly at 32, I saw him after he died.

"Wow that 's young."

Yes, it was horrible. He died in the hospital. He was a doctor and died in the resident's quarters after spending the day in the operating room. It was devastating for me. We were very close. His death from presumed cardiac arrest was especially devastating for me as a heart doctor.

"That is terrible."

When I saw him I wasn't sure of what I was perceiving and wondered if it was in my mind. But I saw an image that looked like him, but I knew that he was not physically alive. Once he talked to me without moving his mouth or lips. It happened in the few days after his death and then it stopped. I actually loved seeing him and had no fear with my visions. I was disappointed when it stopped. I imagine that it was similar to what you experienced when you saw Lucille after she died.

"Right. Exactly."

It was as if there was a short period of time when he was able to manifest into a form that I could see and then it stopped.

"He had to go on to his journey."

He did, and he left. It hasn't happened since then.

"It's too much for humans to conceive. It's far above life, death and the body. It's bigger than that. You go on to another existence. It's interesting to think about coming back. People talk about past lives

This life is a journey. If you don't get it now you will have to come back and get it right. Because we all have to get it right. As Buddha is talking about going towards the light. In our individual time frames, karma, and incarnations. We are all headed towards the light.

I think the universe is so vast that I am making little pecks at knowing what is going on. It's too much to even contemplate."

How can we ever know?

"It's not important to know. Like it's not important to know about past lives. That is a distraction. We don't have time for that. I don't care about that. It is not relevant to my soul development. I have to get myself together now.

People ask me questions like, 'What do you think heaven is like?' I tell them that heaven is right here. There is a reason we are here.

I don't care about the body or what happens to it. It's just dust. Once my spirit, soul leaves here, I don't care what happens. I don't worry about what happens when I die. It's a waste of time.

Think about how you are living here."

Chapter 14

# Simply Positive

*"The mental causes the physical reaction.*
*You think about it,*
*and you make your body do it."*

There are innumerable things that physicians don't learn in medical school, residency or fellowship training. These valuable things come with years of patient care experience and patient observation. One of the most potent things that I have learned is the fact that our personal thoughts can be the source of much disease and suffering.

Every day patients come to see me with a very frightening concern that something may be terribly wrong with their hearts. This concern alerted them or their family physicians who appropriately referred them to me. Typically, this same concern has significantly and negatively impacted their lives.

They have had concern that they may have a serious life-threatening problem. They fear that they inherited heart disease from their parents or grandparents. Their concerns are magnified because of the memory of someone they know who seemed to be fine until they died suddenly of a heart attack.

These thoughts have been repeated in their heads since the onset of their problem. Usually this creates more of the symptoms that started the concern and sometimes they have other new worrisome symptoms. The thoughts swirl in their heads like a stress tornado wreaking havoc on their minds and on their bodies.

When they finally make it to my office the stress from this fearful thinking is evident in their facial expressions and body language. I can usually perceive their distressed energy as soon as they walk into the waiting room in my small office.

Oftentimes our evaluation reveals that their symptoms are the result of high blood pressure or symptoms of another common treatable condition. I am very fortunate to be able to give good news to patients on most occasions. Since high blood pressure and many other conditions are successfully treated with lifestyle changes, diet, exercise, meditation and with medication if needed, the patient is able to immediately relax and rejoice because they have learned that their life is not acutely in danger.

In a short period of time the energy and the feel of the space in the room changes as the patient relaxes. The impact is profound and easy to sense during the course of the evaluation.

Observing this process repeatedly in my office over the last twenty-six years of practice has made me aware of the power of our thoughts. Many people express their belief that many physical problems are expected and planned for as they age.

The concepts that most people hold regarding getting older are typically a bad collection of bad expectations. There is an entire encyclopedia of negative thoughts that includes expectations of becoming less physically capable, less mentally capable, sick, decrepit, dependent, immobile and frail. These thoughts become plans and intentions for most people.

There is error in this reasoning. Studies of radioactively tagged molecules have shown us that 98% of every atom in our body is replaced in one year by atoms that we take in as air, food and drink. This data was presented in the Annual Report of the Smithsonian Institute 1953. The concept that our body is static and that we eat and drink to fuel this static machine is false. We actually eat, drink and take in our environment to remake our bodies constantly.

There is a constant flow of molecules which are

comprised of energy. Nothing is static. Our body appears to be immobile on the outside when we are sitting still. But this is not the case. Patients in my office have the opportunity to see their hearts beating on the echocardiogram which is a sound wave image. They are able to see their heart muscle, the four chambers of the heart and the valves working. It is impressive to see the constant motion and work of the heart while they lie calmly on the exam table. The product of this work is the pumping of blood to every cell of the body at a very high rate.

If a tagged molecule is injected in the vein in one arm, that same molecule will travel to the heart, to the lungs, back to the heart, and then can be pumped to the other arm or anywhere else in the body in 15 seconds.

There is a constant flow of impulses from the brain to the nervous system maintaining sensory motor and autonomic functions all over our bodies.

Our thoughts moment to moment are impacting these functions in real time. It is crucially important that we manage our thoughts to provide the most positive, nurturing, encouraging, healthy, inspired, and creative environment.

Not only do we benefit from avoiding negative thought we are empowered by positive thought. We are strengthened and reinforced by positive behavior.

Studies done in the 70's and 80's suggested that forced smiling changes your perception in a positive manner. More recent studies have shown that a forced smile decreases the physiologic response to stress. People who were forced to perform a task while holding chopsticks in their mouths forcing a smile, had less of a stress response that was measured by an increase in their heart rate. The assumption of the investigators was that a smile, even a fake smile can help to reduce the bodies stress response.

By decreasing the stress response, smiling can improve immunity because stress clearly reduces immunity. In addition, one study showed that patients with advanced cancer, on chemotherapy who participated in laughter therapy had higher levels of markers that indicate immune function.

Sonny has a constant internal dialogue that is encouraging and open. He finds a way to be the same which is good no matter what is happening internally or externally. His constant positive flow, sense of humor and his laugh are infectious.

Sonny! How is your Friday?

"Well, my Friday is okay. There's a lot of little things happening. Since we are on the planet, we are going to experience certain things that go with being alive and being here. We are going through our karmic journey. But, there is nothing to complain about."

When you say that I know that you must be going through something that you don't like.

What's going on?

"Ha, ha, ha, ha.... you are very intuitive. It's nothing really. I don't want to talk about it because it exaggerates it. I'm ashamed to even admit to any negativity. I don't want to voice a negative thought because it will give it more power. I am done with it and it doesn't deserve more energy or time from me. When it comes to the big picture it is absolutely shameful for me to admit any negativity at all. Do you know what I mean?"

I do. I advise my patients to monitor what they say and what they think because they are creating their experience at that moment. As soon as you start thinking or saying things like, "I am s-a-d." I spelled it because I won't say it now. Or commonly people say, "I am t-i-r-e-d"

"Or s-i-c-k. That is one I hear very frequently."

Yes! That is a common powerfully negative statement. Thinking it has bad effects and saying it is worse. When you say it you thought it, said it and then heard the words out loud as you said it!

Immediately you feel more s-i-c-k, or t-i-r-e-d, or s-a-d. Those words carry the energy of their meaning.

When we say them, there is an entire encyclopedia in our memories that moves into play and action. These negative self-descriptions enhance and reinforce these sensations. Conversely, if you have a thought along these lines and you replace it with a thought or a comment like;

I am great. I am powerful. I am healthy.

Immediately you feel the energy of these words. It is crucial to follow "I AM" with something that you want to be. Words and thoughts have energy and the power to model your physical and emotional sensations.

There is a seamless connection between your words and thoughts with your mind and body reaction to them. The more you say and think these negative things the more you create these energies in your physical being.

"That is the way it happens. I feel the difference in my consciousness. I know that there is no value in giving energy and time to negative things. It makes them grow. I don't want to give energy to these things that we deal with here on earth. I am interested in the big picture. I am interested in the universe."

There are immense benefits to not only thinking and speaking positively, acting like you are happy can make you happy. Smiling improves your immunity. This is true even if the smile is a fake forced smile. Isn't that fascinating?

"I can see that. It makes those around you feel happy. All that energy is connected. We are all connected."

I've tried to imagine how this happens. Maybe a fake smile can evoke memories and sensations of times in the past when you had real smiles and tap into that positive energy. So, it seems that it would help in a situation when you think you might be getting sick, or stressed, you should purposefully smile a lot. No matter how you feel.

"That's funny. But it's true. When you tell people things like that they don't believe it. But, it's true, positive thoughts and words help. You have to live like that. The mental causes the physical reaction. You think about it and you make your body do it.

I have experienced the power of my thoughts. If I concentrate on a part of my body intensely, I can begin to feel a vibrating sensation in that part of my body. If I have a toothache and concentrate on sending a bright light of energy to that tooth. The tooth will stop hurting. It has worked for me.

I have been aware of the power of thoughts for a long time. People do not realize the power that they have to create things with their thoughts. You can create bad things with bad thoughts and good things with good thoughts."

Thoughts are intentions. You are the creator and the director of your thoughts and of your life.

You must manage your thoughts and your words. A concept that I learned in my courses is that worrying is like praying for what you don't want. When you hold these negative things in your consciousness you make bad things happen to your mind and your body.

"There is so much to learn here. I am learning every day. We are all students. I don't consider myself to be a teacher. I am still learning. I thank the heavenly forces that every day I have another opportunity in this world to learn. Remember the story that I told you about the two birds? That was from *The Upanishads*."

Yes. That is one of the books in my curriculum for my courses. I loved your version of that story.

"It is part of the wonderful knowledge of Vedanta. You can't make me a teacher I am a learner."

Every teacher is a student. The teacher that stops learning is doomed. We are all learning.

The best teachers are always striving to learn more and grow. The most intelligent people are humble about what they know and appreciate the vast things that they do not know.

It is a great experience when you help people along to learn the things that you have learned and then take them along with you as you learn more. The process is educational for all involved.

"All teachers say that they learn from the students. I hope that others can learn from the things that I have learned. I hope that it will help people."

I've noted that the energy of the learning environment appears to be infectious. Since I started my classes some people around me have been inspired to study. My receptionist, Sonja, has been inspired to get a certification in Yoga asanas.

"Hatha yoga."

Yes. She has said that she was surprised at how easy it

was for her to study. She has been inspired and she wants the knowledge. She had forgotten how fun it is to be a student.

When you are inspired and excited by the knowledge, it is fun.

"Well I hope so because you are helping people. You have to keep doing what you are doing.

Are you taking care of yourself?"

After my busy week, yesterday morning I was feeling a bit tired. Unfortunately, I turned on the news, and heard a lot of bad news. I could feel it disturbing my calm. It was disturbing my peace. I decided that I had to detach from it. Turn it off. I chose something creative instead, writing.

I started writing the book yesterday.

"That is wonderful.

It's all good. You are on the path, on the journey. That is where it's at. There is an infinite place out there where we are destined to go. Congratulations."

While sharing these kinds of thoughts and this wisdom, it will help other people to move on in that journey. It is a wonderful thing to be able to help other people to step into that flow. That is where I want to take them. I have so many things to write about. I have notes from way back before we talked about a book. I wrote down things that you said to me because they meant so much to me.

So, I have plenty to read and write. I feel that I have entered a whole new flow. It's like riding on a new tide. I feel that this tide just came in and got me. I know that it will flow easily and happen naturally. Just like my classes and certifications happened naturally. It was work but it was not laborious. It was exactly the right work. So it feels good.

"Well, you are in the flow. That's it. You are doing something positive. You are doing what you are supposed to be doing. We are on a journey here and we are heading toward the light. Instead of trying to figure out what this world is about. We have to stay positive and be sure that what we are doing is positive. You can't let the bad happenings and news turn you negative. Staying positive is your calling. You have to find what you are meant to be doing of a positive nature and focus on that. That is what you are called to do."

I agree. I think that when you are not going in the right direction working hard becomes laborious work. I had many thoughts about our first conversations. I have been recalling many of the very first concepts that you shared with me. Since then I have been studying ancient texts and found words that are similar to your words in many of these beautiful books. It's like a big circle.

"You know you are right, like a circle. But when I think about it I think about a spiral. It's a circle but it is going up.

I have been thinking about these things for a long time. It makes sense. Up higher to more elevated levels of understanding. More elevated levels of energy and consciousness."

# Chapter 15

# Giving

*"You are acting with a good spirit,
and universal truth,
giving and trying to help others.
Whatever happens is small world stuff.
Big world stuff is
that you did it with good intentions."*

Sonny does not settle or rest on his past achievements. He considers himself to be constantly in progress. He spends his time improving his knowledge and his awareness while taking opportunities to give to others.

He sent a personal letter to Barbara Boxer to let her know that he appreciated her work. She appeared to be very touched by his letter. In her farewell speech on 12-07-16 she tearfully said:

"I've often joked about some of the things that have been said to me over the years that are too colorful in a negative way to repeat here. But I want everyone to know, whether friend or foe, whether critic or admirer, I do appreciate the fact, that you let me know, how you felt about my work, one way or the other. So, to close, I want to read into the record a letter I received in October from one of the greatest Jazz musicians in our country, Sonny Rollins. It was a hand-written letter. He was recently honored at the Kennedy Center and he writes in longhand and I quote him.

'Greetings. So, so sorry that we are not going to have you for us anymore. I've always been interested in politics, marching as a six-year old with my activist grandmother for civil rights. It has been such a joy and inspiration knowing that Barbara Boxer was there for us. God bless you, your family, and loved ones and thank you. You will be missed and we all love you. Have a beautiful life just like you have made life beautiful for so many citizens.'

Well I want to thank Sonny Rollins. I don't know him personally. I met him once. But what he said is all that I wanted to do to make life beautiful for people."

Sonny told me about his letter in one of our conversations some time later.

"Chris, did I tell you about the letter that I sent to Barbara Boxer? I met her at the White House some years ago. When I heard she was retiring, I wrote her a letter thanking her for her work on behalf of the underdog. A couple of months later, I got a handwritten letter from her saying that the letter had made her happy and that she would read it into the congressional record on her farewell speech. She read it and I heard that she got kind of emotional when she read it."

Yes. You touched her. Lots of people work hard doing good things for others all of the time. There is something very special about knowing that people see you and know that you are there. Everybody has to be inspired and have a purpose. She did a lot of good work and you probably brought it all home. She had been doing exactly what she was meant to be doing.

"That is what she said. She started out trying to help other people. There is a presence, but it can be so difficult in our world. It's like a veil that is separating us from the reality of the big picture. This is not random. Hearing what she said I know that there is a connection. I meant it when I wrote it and she got it."

She definitely got it.

"She has always been trying to help. I didn't want anything in return. When I wrote that to her I was not sure that she would get it. These congresspeople get a lot of foolish mail.

So, I did not expect anything. And I was quite surprised when she sent me a handwritten letter in return."

She mentioned that your note was hand-written too. It's common that people do things that are for the benefit of others. When you become aware that your efforts have made an impact, it is food for the heart and soul.

How are your projects going?

"I've been very busy. I'm still trying to get my archives project done. This was supposed to have been done last summer but we had some problems. But we are back on track now. It's been a lot of work going through my collection. I'm feeling worn out from it."

You have to take your own advice and rest when you are feeling worn out.

"Yeah, yeah, ha, ha, ha, ha.... I know. After it's done I will be able to relax. I also have the scholarship that I am working on for underprivileged kids. These are kids that are low income but really talented."

What a great idea.

"Well it's good to leave something for some talented, low income students. I want to give them a chance to get a leg up in the world. But also, implicit in the scholarship, they have to be good people. They have to understand the spiritual practices of being good to other people. Treating other people well. Giving back."

Is that in the description of the scholarship?

"Yes. As part of the scholarship, at certain times of the year, they will have to give back in some way. Like working in a nursing home or soup kitchen. This will be part of their work. They have to demonstrate that it is more about giving than it is about getting."

If they are as you have described, super talented, they will have a lot to give, even if they don't know it yet.

"Exactly, they have a lot to give. They have been blessed by having this great talent.

Now what do you do with it? Do you just use it for your own aggrandizement, your own benefit?

No. You have to realize that there is more to life than just being feted and honored for being a great musician and all that stuff. All that is good but that is not enough. It's not enough.

This trip that we are on in this life, we have to do more than that. We have to realize more than that. We've got to accomplish more than that."

This is a great concept for a scholarship.

"It will be at Oberlin College and Conservatory in Ohio. Oberlin has a long history of being a leader in social justice. They are the first institution that had a black student to matriculate. Also, the first university to admit a woman. They were involved in the underground railroad trying to get slaves out of the United States. It has a great history of fighting for social justice for years."

Will the scholarship have your name on it?

"Yes. It will be my scholarship with my name. But it's not about me so much. I know it has to be somewhat but that is not the point. The point is that these kids get an opportunity to gain some knowledge at an early stage of their life. And use their gifts in the optimum way that they can.

They've got a gift, now use it in get the most out of it. And really, be helping other people. Then it all comes together. It's all good."

This is how they can continue to elevate their energy level too. And continue to replenish their spiritual and creative forces.

"Absolutely. You said it."

If they start out with that understanding from the beginning, it will make it so much easier and much more productive for them and everyone that listens to them.

"Yes. It will make their lives important in a far greater way, and their karma will be closer to the light. I'm working on my archives and on this project at the same time."

It's seems that when you are truly inspired to do something, you really can't completely relax until it is done. You want to meet that goal. It's truly being called to action.

"Yes, but in a way, it's not really that important. It's small stuff that I am doing while I am here on this planet. It is important in this world but not in the real picture."

But as you have said many times, we are here for a

reason. You have been inspired to do these two things. That is part of your human purpose and there is some spiritual growth or spiritual evolution that happens through that. Or maybe just part of the evolution of the whole human consciousness. But, there is certainly a reason for it.

"Absolutely."

The fact that you are inspired to do it means you are in-spirit. It comes from your spirit. Your spirit calls you.

"Yes. It's a good reason. It's about giving. I was always a very generous person just by nature.

And I had to stop one day and find out whether I was being generous just to make myself feel good or was I really being generous because I wanted the party or the recipient to be happy.

I put myself through several tests and I gladly realized that I want other people to be happy. I am not doing it for myself. It's about others. Once I came to this conclusion, I felt much better about myself."

That is true giving and detachment from it. There is energy in the act of giving itself. Whether the gift is appreciated, does not change the positive energy associated with your action. The action or the gift stands alone in value and positive energy.

"That is true. The act and the intention of giving were involved. That spiritual energy is what it is all about."

The result doesn't matter either. Your part is done. You

taught me that Sonny. You do your best, and then detach.

"That's right. You are acting with a good spirit and universal truth, giving and trying to help others. Whatever happens is small world stuff. Big world stuff is that you did it with good intentions."

That takes away a lot of struggle. If you only have to worry about what you are doing, what your actions are, what your thoughts and intentions are then it is much easier. If you can always focus on doing the right thing and detach then it is simple. I have always found it to be easy to do the right thing. It's hard for me to do the wrong thing and then be concerned about it.

"They say that living a spiritual life is really easy, but it's easy for people who can understand what it is about. This is not easy for everybody. Like when people lie, it's hard because you have to keep remembering what you said and how to clean up for that lie. It's better to be simple and tell the truth. That is a perfect example."

What is the value in that. Honesty is so much easier. No matter what, just deal with it and own it. The truth is the truth.

"Yes, and then you don't have to worry about, oh geez.... what did I say, how did I say it? In some ways they say the spiritual life is easy because you are just doing what you are put here to do."

If your projects kept you from resting this week, you should rest this weekend.

"Well yes, I don't have to get out today. I had to get out this week in inclement weather to get some things signed for this project. How's the weather there?"

It's perfect today, 68 degrees, clear sky, it's gorgeous.

"You know at one time we considered buying a house in the Virgin Gorda. We used to go every winter. There were some American's there that we hung out with. Their problem was that since every day was so beautiful, blue skies, maybe a little shower in the afternoon, it got to be monotonous for them. So, they wanted to sell their house and move back to Ohio."

I get spoiled here in California. But the weather here is not lost on me. Every time that I walk outside and see this gorgeous sky and feel the crisp but not cold weather, I am very grateful.

I could live in that Virgin Gorda house and be very happy. I love nature and pull its value into my awareness regularly. I am grateful for the yellow flowers that I see out my window right now. I live in gratitude and I try to not miss those opportunities.

"When you are in gratitude you are on a different level. I am not saying that you are better or anything like that. I'm not putting anyone down. People come to this planet with different levels of consciousness. We all have to learn and to grow. I am just saying that you are on a different karmic level when you are grateful."

I am grateful for being able to appreciate that there are different levels of awareness.

We all come here with our own set of experiences and memories that is the bases of our interpretation of everything. Our responses to all of our experiences depend on our spiritual growth. I am grateful to be able to have this conversation about these things.

In my class we talk about perception and gratitude. I told my class that when you find yourself in a bad place, think about the simplest things for which you can be grateful. You can start with the clean air we are breathing. The clean water that is easily available. Consider gratitude for the amazing beating heart inside your body that is working every second of every day. This miraculous organ is beating constantly to support our physical lives. It provides oxygenated blood to our entire bodies every moment of every day.

"That is a great lesson."

My point for them was that it is very easy to find something to be grateful for. And the moment that you are grateful, your energy is elevated. When you are sitting in the energy of gratitude, no matter what perceived issue you may have in your world, immediately that issue can become far less important to you.

"Amen. What you are telling me today is beyond beautiful. That is wonder."

If you can be aware of the miraculous things that are

present every moment, particular circumstances are not necessary to feel happy. This is where you find joy. It's a state of being.

"I know I talk to people and they have many problems. Of course, most people can get overwhelmed. There is much opportunity to overcome that."

I have learned to detach from outcomes and to detach from things that are not in my control. Nobody has the universe in their own control. But we all have our personal perceptions in our control. No matter what the problem is, our perception molds how we feel. If the perception is negative you must find a way to detach and file it. You must be happy with your best. Your best is all that you have. You helped me with that Sonny.

"This is good. As long as I am on the planet, I have to keep being reinforced. That is why whenever we talk about these things it is good. It is so easy to be distracted by the negativity of this world."

And our human brains that generate thoughts that are not helpful. Especially when things don't go the way that you want them to go.

"That is why when I talk, I want to talk about spiritual things. That is what makes me happy. This world can be full of noise. I know we are here for a reason. We are here to go through things and to learn but I don't want to get stuck in it.

Remember, I am learning myself. I have to be reinforced with proper knowledge, proper thoughts, proper ideas every day. You have to deal against all that is in the world.

Every day I am trying to get right on the point.

I had a hard life at times and don't like to think about that but I know I had to go through those things. I have been blessed to be able to have seen the light. Not only am I blessed, I am thankful.

During the day I pray a lot. I am always in prayer, really. I am grateful."

Chapter 16

# Blessings

*"It's a lifetime that it's taken me*
*to get the little bit of knowledge*
*that I've accumulated.*
*And that's great.*
*I know that I am on a journey,*
*and the journey is going in the right*
*direction.*
*And.....it's all good."*

It is easy to sense Sonny's open, beautiful spiritual nature when looking into his eyes, in person or in photographs. I saw this many years ago on my mother's canvas. It was a look that called to me, as if to say, "I have something to tell you." The journey which started with my father's friendship in

1976, and the incidents that led to this day, were all part of a plan. It was easy to go with the flow that has resulted in this book.

Sonny has been an integral part of my growth. There were many inspirations that came to me in words and phrases throughout my daily life. When we have our conversations these words and phrases evolve into clear thoughts and sentences. This is an incredible gift and process.

It has been an honor to be able to share Sonny's special wisdom with his fans who have a true appreciation for him and his music. He has taken them soaring on journeys with magically sequenced musical notes that danced like ribbons in the air, with melodic swirls and explosive bursts. These sounds created waves of positive emotions. Musical notes were initially sensed in the ears but felt in the heart and the soul. Countless musical excursions were beautifully navigated on Sonny's horn. He took millions of people beyond this world to intangible brilliant places.

It is my hope that people who felt his spiritual power in the form of his music will elevate their knowledge and their energy in the vibration of his words.


Sonny, before long, I'm going to send you the things that I have written so that I can know that you approve. I have captured many of our conversations.

"Well I hope you remember them because I do things

very spontaneously. So, I don't write things down."

I know you don't.

"Don't ask me, Sonny, what did you say on Friday?"

Don't worry......... I have an excellent memory. Documenting your words is a part of my plan.

"Well I hope it will be beneficial to some people."

I know it will. I am going to send it to you. I want your approval.

"Anything I say to you in our conversations, things of spiritual relevance, is all good."

I know it is going to be very useful. I feel such a calling to do that for other people. I have been graced by our conversations for a long time and I feel a calling to share it with others. I have immense gratitude for my journey. I am grateful for our friendship and for our conversations, grateful for my journey that resulted in teaching Perfect Health and meditation, grateful for the skills and desires that allowed me to be a cardiologist.

"You have been blessed. What you are doing is so fantastic and it is important. It is what is needed in this lifetime. Keep doing what you are doing. You can't help it now because it is so much a part of your essence. Everything that you do is part of you. In a way you can say you've been chosen. People used to say that you have been chosen. The supreme divinity has chosen you, whatever you say, you have been touched by the spirit."

Called, or given the opportunity. It was the next step. I've been taking care of people's hearts for a long time. Now I have an opportunity to help people in an entirely different way. I am lucky, very lucky.

"Oh boy. Well I'd rather say you are blessed. You can say you are lucky if you want."

I am blessed. I feel that energy every day. One of the very first things you told me was, It's all good.

"That is right. You know it is. It's all good. It can be hard in this world. It's easy to lose sight and to think about things in the little pool instead of the big ocean. The big ocean is eternity.

The infinite is all good. The finite is the small picture. This stuff down here in our world, we have to go through it. We are here, so we have to do it. We have to learn and try to do it right and try to get it right. This might seem that it is not good at times. The big picture is eternity, infinity, universal. We just have to get it in our world. Now you've got it. You've been blessed with so many attributes that have been bestowed upon you. I can feel your light."

It's funny that you say that because when I first saw you perform, I saw your light. I will never forget that.

"I don't remember when that was."

It was when I brought my Mom to see you perform in California. When you got on the stage, I felt the most amazing energy. Almost like a vibration. I had never felt that before a concert. The performance was exceptional, but what shocked me was this energy that I could sense, this high vibration. It was phenomenal.

Then after the show my goal was to get Mom back there to say hello. I had to figure out a way to make it happen. I asked an attendant for directions and she directed us down stairs around the building around to the back entry to the backstage steps. (Laughing) So I took mom back there and we had to walk around all these big trucks.

"Oh boy. This is terrible."

(Still laughing) It was funny Sonny. It was like an obstacle course. But I was determined. We went up, down around. Tried many doors until we finally got in.

The interesting thing is that I was motivated to get my mother back to see you to say hello. At that time, I had no idea about the source of the energy that I felt in that moment. At this time, I know that I felt a connection. That was the beginning.

"That's wonderful."

I remember it like it was yesterday.

"Well you know there is no time really. We make up the dimension of time. Time, age, people, life, death doesn't exist. We make it all up."

It's so hard to wrap the brain around that concept.

"Yes, in the small karmic world that we live in, it is very hard to realize this. But it is the universal picture that is the reality. It's all there way beyond time."

If you are able to grasp that it makes the little stuff seem suddenly silly.

"Well we know that it is silly to think that anything is not good. But we have to go through it all. I believe in karma. We have to go through our karma. It is part of this world.

I am just thinking about the universal picture. That is the only thing that really means anything to me. What am I here for? What's the point? What am I supposed to be doing?"

Those are soul questions. Through inquiry we get answers to these questions.

"That's what it's all about. Of course, I've been here for a while on this planet. People can say to me, 'That's easy for you to say.' Nevertheless, it's true. Am I here to eat more ice cream? That's nobody's purpose in life. That's giving in to physical senses.

This is really a short life. Many of my friends have already transitioned. We don't have a lot of time here. If you believe in afterlife you don't have to feel that you have to do everything in this life. You don't have to.

Just make sure that this one is good as it can be. Giving to people and helping people. Life is going to be over in a minute anyway. But those things your soul takes with it. I will get through this life and go on to the next. If my theory is correct, I will have a little more knowledge.

A little more enlightenment. I will be a little further along the path. You know the Buddha talked about the path and the light. If I am correct, I will be going toward the light.

All I can go by is, do unto others as you would have them do unto you. This is what I am sure to do now. It doesn't matter what the future holds."

Enlightenment?

"I am not as enlightened as I want to be. It's my goal to do unto others as I would have them do unto me. It's my goal to be a giving person. It's my goal to be a kind person. It's my goal to help others. These are my goals. So, I don't see myself as having accomplished everything in these areas, but I understand that this is where I want to go. I am thankfully on that path."

In regard to your actions in this world, Sonny, is there anything that you wish that you had done, or anything that you were not able to do?

"No. Because, you know, I think it's sort of blasphemy to think like that. Well gees, I should of done this or could of....... no, no. My life was made for a reason. It happened for a reason just the way it is. And if there is anything that caused regrets, then I will do it next time around.

There is no reason to regret. If you didn't get it now you will get it later. The guy said pay me now or pay me later. Who knows how many lives we have lived. I don't need to think about that.

It is beyond my ability to understand. All I need is to try

to be kind and help other people.

Try not to steal things from anybody or to hurt people. That is for one lifetime. If I do that then I will take care of this lifetime."

One thing that is lovely in this lifetime is that you created a mechanism for people to connect with their spirits through your music. What a beautiful gift to give.

"Well yes. But I can't take credit for my music. I don't say, me, me. That was a gift. Any talent you have is a gift. I don't say, oh boy, I did this. I played my horn....no, no! I was part of the big picture, just like you are a part of the big picture.

I was meant to help people in any way that I could with any opportunities that I had available to me. My music was a gift that I was given to share. I did my little part. That was the universal power that was given to me to help them.

The part that I am trying to do now is to help people to get some understanding, some enlightenment. That is what I am called to do now."

It is good to be in the place in which you know this to be the truth.

"It's pretty good. And it's a lifetime that it's taken me to get the little bit of knowledge that I have accumulated. And that's great.

So, I know that I'm on a journey and the journey is going in the right direction.

And…. it's all good!"

# Acknowledgments

This book exists because of Sonny's desire to give. I am grateful for all that he has given to me and for sharing with others. His friendship has been a formidable positive force in my life in many ways and the impact he has had on my life is beyond what I can express in words. Thank you, Sonny.

*It's All Good* rapidly evolved from computer files to a published book with the herculean efforts of my family team. My deepest thank you to these devoted caring people who love me and love Sonny. They believed in this project and fearlessly volunteered their help to bring it to fruition.

My mother, Yvonne Theard was an outstanding editor. Her inspiring painting of Sonny that is on our cover is an awesome work that has captured my spirit for many years. My daughter, Tina Kirby found time in the midst of her busy work managing my medical office and caring for my three grandsons to eagerly volunteer to create the perfect cover design. Thank you to my love, Ory Conrad for his tireless formatting, technical expertise and continuous support.

Great thanks to my father, Les Theard for his many contributions, his enthusiam and his friendship with Sonny that started it all. Thank you to my brother, Paul Theard for his editing. Thank you to my brother Norm Theard and my son, Luke Ronnie for being core members of my team.

Thank you to all the family, friends and patients who were excited about this project and encouraged me to proceed. Thank you to Chuck Stewart for the photo that inspired the cover painting and to Kim Stewart for allowing us to use the painting. Thank you to Deepak Chopra and the extraordinary Chopra Center staff for my education and certification in Perfect Health and Primordial Sound Meditation. Finally, thank you to my talented superstar friend, Mindi Abair for giving me advice that took us to the finish line.

# About the Author

Christine M. Theard, M.D. is a cardiologist with 26 years of practice experience and a Chopra certified instructor of Perfect Health and Primordial Sound Meditation. She is the mother of five children, including triplets, and lives with her family in Dana Point, California.

Backstage with Sonny on September 25, 2011,
Sergerstrom Center for the Arts, Costa Mesa, California.